PERMUTATION GROUPS

Mathematics Lecture Note Series

E. Artin and J. Tate *Harvard University*	CLASS FIELD THEORY
Michael Atiyah *Oxford University*	K-THEORY
Hyman Bass *Columbia University*	ALGEBRAIC K-THEORY
Raoul Bott *Harvard University*	LECTURES ON K(X)
Paul J. Cohen *Stanford University*	SET THEORY AND THE CONTINUUM HYPOTHESIS
Walter Feit *Yale University*	CHARACTERS OF FINITE GROUPS
Marvin J. Greenberg *Northeastern University*	LECTURES ON ALGEBRAIC TOPOLOGY
Robin Hartshorne *Harvard University*	FOUNDATIONS OF PROJECTIVE GEOMETRY
Irving Kaplansky *University of Chicago*	RINGS OF OPERATORS
Serge Lang *Columbia University*	ALGEBRAIC FUNCTIONS
Serge Lang *Columbia University*	RAPPORT SUR LA COHOMOLOGIE DES GROUPES
I. G. Macdonald *Oxford University*	ALGEBRAIC GEOMETRY: INTRODUCTION TO SCHEMES
George Mackey *Harvard University*	INDUCED REPRESENTATIONS OF GROUPS AND QUANTUM MECHANICS
Richard Palais *Brandeis University*	FOUNDATIONS OF GLOBAL NON-LINEAR ANALYSIS
Donald Passman *Yale University*	PERMUTATION GROUPS
Jean-Pierre Serre *Collège de France*	ABELIAN *l*-ADIC REPRESENTATIONS AND ELLIPTIC CURVES
Jean-Pierre Serre *Collège de France*	ALGEBRES DE LIE SEMI-SIMPLES COMPLEXES
Jean-Pierre Serre *Collège de France*	LIE ALGEBRAS AND LIE GROUPS

PERMUTATION GROUPS

DONALD PASSMAN

Yale University

W. A. Benjamin, Inc.

New York 1968 Amsterdam

PERMUTATION GROUPS

Library of Congress Catalog Card Number 68-55989
Manufactured in the United States of America

*The manuscript was put into production on June 20, 1968;
this volume was published on September 27, 1968.*

W. A. BENJAMIN, INC.
New York, New York 10016

A Note from the Publisher

This volume was printed directly from a typescript prepared by the author, who takes full responsibility for its content and appearance. The Publisher has not performed his usual functions of reviewing, editing, typesetting, and proofreading the material prior to publication.

The Publisher fully endorses this informal and quick method of publishing lecture notes at a moderate price, and he wishes to thank the author for preparing the material for publication.

PREFACE

These are the lecture notes from a rather crowded one-term course I gave at Yale University in the spring of 1967. My aim at that time was to give a self-contained account of certain classification theorems in the field of permutation groups. These are theorems which are frequently quoted and yet are reasonably inaccessible. In particular I refer to the work of Zassenhaus on Frobenius complements and sharply transitive groups, and to the work of Huppert on solvable doubly transitive groups. The students were assumed to be familiar with elementary group theory, linear algebra, and Galois theory, or in other words with material covered in a basic course in modern algebra.

Chapter I, although introductory in nature, does contain several non-trivial results. One such example is Wielandt's slick new proof of Burnside's theorem on permutation groups of prime degree. Another is Wielandt's theorem on the finiteness of automorphism towers.

Chapter II is devoted to developing the tools of basic group theory in a most economical manner. Thus we cover topics such as group extensions and transfer and representation theory but only to the extent that they will be needed later.

Chapter III starts with a fairly complete study of Frobenius groups. We prove Thompson's theorem on the nilpotence of Frobenius kernels and we obtain Zassenhaus' classification of the complements. Next we give a new proof of Huppert's result on solvable doubly transitive groups. Finally we classify the sharply transitive permutation groups, concluding with Witt's construction of the Mathieu groups.

I would like to thank Mrs. Madeline Delaney for her fine typing of the original lecture notes.

D. S. PASSMAN

NEW HAVEN, CONNECTICUT
JUNE 1968

CONTENTS

CHAPTER I

INTRODUCTION

1. THE SYMMETRIC GROUP

Let A be a finite set and let $\mathrm{Sym}\ A$ for the moment denote the set of one to one functions from A onto A. If $a \in A$ and $f \in \mathrm{Sym}\ A$, then we denote by af the image of the element a. If $f, g \in \mathrm{Sym}\ A$, then we define the function fg by $a(fg) = (af)g$. It is easy to see that $\mathrm{Sym}\ A$ with this composition multiplication forms a group, the symmetric group on set A.

Let A and B be two finite sets of the same size. Then there is an obvious isomorphism of $\mathrm{Sym}\ A$ with $\mathrm{Sym}\ B$ which commutes with the given one to one correspondence between the two sets. Thus it suffices to choose a fixed set of each finite size. Given integer $n \geq 1$, if $A = \{1, 2, \ldots, n\}$ then we write Sym(n) for Sym A. A permutation group is a subgroup of Sym(n). Here n is its degree.

Let $f \in \mathrm{Sym}(n)$ so that f is uniquely determined by the set of ordered pairs $\{(a, af)\}$ where $a = 1, 2, \ldots, n$. We tilt these ordered pairs by a quarter turn and write a above af. Moreover we place all these n expressions adjacent to each other and have

$$f = \begin{pmatrix} 1 & 2 & & n \\ & & \cdots & \\ 1f & 2f & & nf \end{pmatrix} = \begin{pmatrix} a \\ \\ af \end{pmatrix}.$$

This correspondence is one to one provided we understand that the information contained in the symbol $\binom{a}{af}$ is just the relationship of the first row to the second. Thus the ordering of the columns is unimportant. For example with $n = 3$ we have

$$\begin{pmatrix} 1 & 2 & 3 \\ \\ 3 & 1 & 2 \end{pmatrix} = \begin{pmatrix} 1 & 3 & 2 \\ \\ 3 & 2 & 1 \end{pmatrix}.$$

Using this fact we can obtain an easy rule of multiplication.

Given $f, g \in \mathrm{Sym}(n)$ and let

$$f = \begin{pmatrix} a \\ \\ af \end{pmatrix} \qquad g = \begin{pmatrix} a \\ \\ ag \end{pmatrix}.$$

We reorder the columns of $\begin{pmatrix} a \\ ag \end{pmatrix}$ until the top row looks like the bottom row of $\begin{pmatrix} a \\ af \end{pmatrix}$. Then

$$g = \begin{pmatrix} af \\ \\ (af)g \end{pmatrix} = \begin{pmatrix} af \\ \\ a(fg) \end{pmatrix}$$

and

$$fg = \begin{pmatrix} a \\ \\ a(fg) \end{pmatrix} = \begin{pmatrix} a \\ \\ \cancel{af} \end{pmatrix} \begin{pmatrix} \cancel{af} \\ \\ a(fg) \end{pmatrix}.$$

Hence if the columns are properly ordered, multiplication essentially amounts to cancellation.

Now the symbol $\begin{pmatrix} a \\ af \end{pmatrix}$ is not typographically convenient. Moreover it does not always show clearly the effect of the function. A more graphical notation is to write f as a product of cycles. Given f and choose any $a \in \{1, 2, \ldots, n\}$. The cycle of f which starts with a is

$$(a \;\; af \;\; af^2 \;\; \ldots \;\; af^{r-1})$$

where r is minimal with $af^r = a$. Since Sym(n) is a finite group such an integer r exists. By the minimality of r it is easy to see that all the elements in this cycle are distinct. We say that two cycles are the same if one can be obtained from the other by circularly shifting the elements. For example the cycles (1 2 3 4 5) and (3 4 5 1 2) are the same. With this convention we see easily that any two cycles of f are either the same or disjoint, that is have no elements in common. We write the distinct cycles of f adjacent to each other on a line in any order and we use this as an alternate notation for f. For example

$$\begin{pmatrix} 1 & 2 & 3 & 4 & 5 & 6 & 7 & 8 \\ 2 & 3 & 1 & 5 & 4 & 6 & 8 & 7 \end{pmatrix} = (1 \;\; 2 \;\; 3)(4 \;\; 5)(6)(7 \;\; 8).$$

It is obvious that this correspondence is one to one up to the order in which the cycles are written and the choice of the first element of each cycle.

As a short hand we will drop all cycles of length one from this notation. Thus if $(1 \;\; 2 \;\; 3) \in \mathrm{Sym}(5)$, then this function fixes elements 4 and 5. Now consider the permutation

$$\begin{pmatrix} 1 & 2 & 3 & 4 & 5 \\ 2 & 3 & 1 & 5 & 4 \end{pmatrix} = (1\ 2\ 3)(4\ 5).$$

So far we have considered the expression $(1\ 2\ 3)(4\ 5)$ as merely the juxtaposition of cycles $(1\ 2\ 3)$ and $(4\ 5)$. However with the short hand convention $(1\ 2\ 3)$ and $(4\ 5)$ are permutations and thus $(1\ 2\ 3)(4\ 5)$ could mean the product of the two. A little thought will show that juxtaposition and multiplication yield the same result here. Hence we have shown that every permutation can be written as the product of disjoint cycles.

Consider a typical cycle $(a_1 \ldots a_r)$ of length r. We see easily that this element has order r. Also

$$(a_1 \ldots a_r) = (a_1\ a_2)(a_1\ a_3) \ldots (a_1\ a_r)$$

so that this cycle can be written as the product of $r - 1$ transpositions. Here of course a transposition is a cycle of length 2. We note also that two disjoint cycles commute with each other. Thus if

$$f = (\underset{r_1}{\underline{\qquad}})(\underset{r_2}{\underline{\qquad}}) \ldots (\underset{r_j}{\underline{\qquad}})$$

is a product of disjoint cycles, then using $o(f)$ to denote the order of f we have

$$o(f) = \mathrm{lcm}\left\{r_1, r_2, \ldots, r_j\right\}$$

and f can be written as a product of $\sum_1^j (r_i - 1)$ transpositions. In particular the set of transpositions generates Sym(n).

To each permutation f we associate a real number $\sigma(f)$ as follows. If

$$f = \begin{pmatrix} a_1 & a_2 & \ldots & a_n \\ b_1 & b_2 & \ldots & b_n \end{pmatrix}$$

set

$$\sigma(f) = \prod \frac{a_i - a_j}{b_i - b_j}$$

where the product runs over all subsets $\{i, j\}$ of size two. Note that the product expression does not depend on the order of the columns and that the quotient $(a_i - a_j)/(b_i - b_j)$

is in fact a function of the set $\{i, j\}$. Hence $\sigma(f)$ is well defined. We use the cancellative form of permutation multiplication. Write

$$f = \begin{pmatrix} a_1 & \dots & a_n \\ b_1 & \dots & b_n \end{pmatrix} \qquad g = \begin{pmatrix} b_1 & \dots & b_n \\ c_1 & \dots & c_n \end{pmatrix}$$

so that

$$\sigma(f)\ \sigma(g) = \prod \frac{a_i - a_j}{b_i - b_j} \cdot \prod \frac{b_i - b_j}{c_i - c_j}$$

$$\prod \frac{a_i - a_j}{c_i - c_j} = \sigma(fg).$$

Hence σ is a homomorphism of Sym(n) into the multiplicative group of the reals and we denote the kernel by Alt(n), the alternating group of degree n.

Let t be a transposition. We find $\sigma(t)$. It suffices to assume that

$$t = \begin{pmatrix} a_1 & a_2 & a_3 & \dots & a_n \\ a_2 & a_1 & a_3 & \dots & a_n \end{pmatrix}.$$

In this form it is easy to see that

$$\sigma(t) = \frac{(a_2 - a_1)}{(a_1 - a_2)} \prod_{\{i,j\} \neq \{1,2\}} \frac{a_i - a_j}{a_i - a_j} = -1.$$

Since Sym(n) is generated by transpositions we see that $\sigma(f) = +1$ or -1 according to whether f can be written as a product of an even or odd number of transpositions. Obviously this parity is preserved no matter how we write f as a product of transpositions. Thus we speak of even and odd permutations. We see that Alt(n) is the set of all even permutations and that [Sym(n):Alt(n)] = 2.

2. WREATH PRODUCTS

Let G be a permutation group on set A and let H be a permutation group on set B. We assume A and B are disjoint, $|A| = \alpha$ and $|B| = \beta$. It is easy to combine these to get a permutation group on $A \cup B$. Let $K = G \times H$, the direct product of G and H. Then every element of K is written uniquely as $[g, h]$ with $g \in G$, $h \in H$. We define the action of K on $A \cup B$ by

$$x[g,h] = \begin{cases} xg & \text{if } x \in A \\ xh & \text{if } x \in B \end{cases}.$$

We see easily that $K \subseteq \mathrm{Sym}\, A \cup B$. Finally $|K| = |G||H|$ and $\deg K = \deg G + \deg H$.

A more complicated situation is the Wreath product. Roughly speaking, we take β copies of G and A, say $G_1, \ldots, G_\beta$, $A_1, \ldots, A_\beta$ with G_i acting on A_i. Then as above we let $G_1 \times G_2 \times \ldots \times G_\beta$ act on $A_1 \cup A_2 \cup \ldots \cup A_\beta$ in the obvious manner. Finally we let H act on $A_1 \cup A_2 \cup \ldots \cup A_\beta$ by permuting the subscripts in the same way that H acts on B. We now describe this more precisely. Let $B = \{b_1, b_2, \ldots, b_\beta\}$ and set $K = G \wr H$, the Wreath product of G and H, in that order. K is a subgroup of $\mathrm{Sym}\, A \times B$ and each element of K is written uniquely as $[g_1, g_2, \ldots, g_\beta; h]$ where $g_i \in G$, $h \in H$. We define the action of K on $A \times B$ by

$$(a, b_i)\,[g_1, g_2, \ldots, g_\beta; h] = (ag_i, b_ih).$$

It is easy to check that K is closed under function composition so that K is indeed a subgroup of $\mathrm{Sym}\, A \times B$.

We see easily that $|K| = |G|^{\beta}|H|$ and $\deg K = (\deg G)(\deg H)$.

Note that if we identify $(A \cup B) \cup C = A \cup (B \cup C)$ and $(A \times B) \times C = A \times (B \times C)$, then products and Wreath products are associative operations.

Let p be a prime and let J be the cyclic subgroup of order p of $\mathrm{Sym}(p)$ generated by the cycle $(1\ 2\ \ldots\ p)$. Thus J has order p and degree p. Then $J \wr J$ has degree p^2 and order p^{1+p}, $J \wr J \wr J$ has degree p^3 and order p^{1+p+p^2} and in general $\underbrace{J \wr J \wr J \wr \ldots \wr J}_{r}$ has degree p^r and order $p^{1+p+\ldots+p^{r-1}}$. For convenience we will write this group as $J^{\wr r}$ with $J^{\wr 0} = \mathrm{Sym}(1)$. Let n be any integer and write

$$n = a_0 + a_1 p + \ldots + a_k p^k$$

where $0 \leq a_i < p$. Then by taking isomorphic copies of the above groups so as to act on different sets we see that

$$S = (\underbrace{J^{\wr 0} \times \ldots \times J^{\wr 0}}_{a_0}) \times (\underbrace{J^{\wr 1} \times \ldots \times J^{\wr 1}}_{a_1}) \times \ldots \times (\underbrace{J^{\wr k} \times \ldots \times J^{\wr k}}_{a_k})$$

$$= \prod (J^{\wr i})^{a_i}$$

has degree $a_0+a_1p+\ldots+a_kp^k = n$ and order $|S|=p^N$ where

$$N = \sum_1^k a_i(1+p+\ldots+p^{i-1}).$$

Now $|\mathrm{Sym}(n)| = n!$ obviously. Let S_p be a Sylow p-subgroup and suppose that $|S_p| = p^M$. Then p^M is the p-part of $n!$. Now there are clearly $[n/p]$ numbers $\le n$ which are divisible by p. Of these $[n/p^2]$ are divisible by p^2 and in general $[n/p^i]$ are divisible by p^i. This implies easily that

$$M = [n/p]+[n/p^2]+[n/p^3]+\ldots..$$

since a number $p^st \le n$ contributes s to the exponent M and also occurs in the first s sets whose sizes are the summands on the right hand side of the above. Using $n = a_0+a_1p+\ldots+a_kp^k$ with $0 \le a_i < p$ we obtain easily

$$M = \sum_1^k a_i(1+p+\ldots+p^{i-1}) = N$$

and hence S is a Sylow p-subgroup of $\mathrm{Sym}(n)$. In this way we have found the Sylow subgroups of the symmetric groups.

3. MULTIPLE TRANSITIVITY

Let G be a permutation group on set A. If $a, b \in A$ we say $a \sim b$ if and only if there exists $g \in G$ with $ag = b$. We see easily that $a \sim b$ is an equivalence relation and we call the equivalence classes the orbits of G. Thus A is the disjoint union of orbits under the action of G. We say G is $1/2$-transitive if all the orbits have the same size and G is transitive if A is an orbit.

If $a \in A$ set $G_a = \{g \in G \mid ag = a\}$ so that G_a is clearly a subgroup of G. We see easily that if $a \in A$, $g \in G$ then

$$G_{ag} = g^{-1}G_a g = G_a{}^g.$$

Suppose $a \sim b$ so that $ah = b$. Then $\{g \mid ag = b\} = G_a h$. Thus if G is transitive then there is a one to one correspondence between the elements of A and the right cosets of G_a given by $G_a h \leftrightarrow b$ if and only if $ah = b$. Hence $|A| = [G:G_a]$.

For each $g \in G$ define $\Theta(g)$ to be the number of $a \in A$ with $ag = a$.

PROPOSITION 3.1. $\sum_{g \in G} \theta(g) = t\,|G|$ where t equals the number of orbits of G.

Proof. It suffices to assume that G is transitive. Consider the set

$$\underline{S} = \{(a, g) \mid a \in A,\ g \in G,\ ag = a\}$$

and we find $|\underline{S}|$ by counting in two different ways. For each $a \in A$ the number of g with $(a, g) \in \underline{S}$ is $|G_a|$. Hence since these groups all have the same size we have $|\underline{S}| = |G_a||A| = |G|$. Now for each $g \in G$ the number of a with $(a, g) \in \underline{S}$ is $\theta(g)$. Hence $\sum \theta(g) = |\underline{S}| = |G|$ and the result follows.

Note that G is 1/2-transitive if and only if $|G_a|$ is the same for all $a \in A$. A special case of this occurs when $G_a = \langle 1 \rangle$ for all $a \in A$. In this case we say that G is semiregular. If in addition G is transitive then we say that G is regular.

PROPOSITION 3.2. Let H be a transitive abelian group.

Then H is regular.

Proof. Fix $a \in A$. If $b \in A$ then there exists $h \in H$ with $ah = b$. Now $H_b = H_{ah} = H_a^h = H_a$ so H_a fixes b. Hence $H_a = \langle 1 \rangle$. Since H is transitive, it is regular.

Let G be transitive. A subset B of A is a subset of imprimitivity if for all $g, h \in G$ we have either $Bg = Bh$ or $Bg \cap Bh = \emptyset$, the empty set. This is equivalent to either $Bg = B$ or $Bg \cap B = \emptyset$. We assume here that $B \neq \emptyset$. If $B = A$ or $|B| = 1$, then certainly B is a subset of imprimitivity. We call these trivial. A group G is said to be imprimitive if it has a nontrivial subset of imprimitivity. Otherwise G is primitive. If B exists then $A = \bigcup Bg$ is a disjoint union and hence $|B| \mid |A|$. This yields

PROPOSITION 3.3. Let G be a transitive permutation group of prime degree. Then G is primitive.

We can tell whether G is primitive or not with the

following result.

PROPOSITION 3.4. Let G be a transitive permutation group. Then G is primitive if and only if G_a is a maximal subgroup.

Proof. Suppose G is imprimitive with nontrivial subset of imprimitivity B. Let $H = \{g \in G \mid Bg = B\}$. Let $a \in B$. If $g \in G_a$ then $a \in B \cap Bg$ so $B = Bg$ and $g \in H$. Hence $G_a \subseteq H \subseteq G$. Since G is transitive and $A \neq B$ we have $H \neq G$. Since $|B| \neq 1$, choose $b \in B$, $b \neq a$. By transitivity there exists $h \in G$ with $ah = b$ so that $h \notin G_a$. Now $b \in B \cap Bh$ so $B = Bh$ and $h \in H - G_a$. Thus $H \neq G_a$ and hence G_a is not a maximal subgroup.

Conversely suppose we have $G_a < H < G$ for some subgroup H. Let $B = aH$. Since $H > G_a$ we have $|B| \neq 1$. If $B = A$ then H is transitive and hence $|A| = [G:G_a] = [H:G_a]$, a contradiction since $G \neq H$. Finally suppose $B \cap Bg \neq \emptyset$ so that $b \in B \cap Bg$. Thus for $h_1, h_2 \in H$ we have $ah_1 = b = ah_2g$ and hence $h_2gh_1^{-1} \in G_a$. This yields $g \in H$

and thus $B = Bg$.

Let m be a positive integer. We say G is m-transitive if given any two ordered subsets $\{a_1, a_2, \ldots, a_m\}$ and $\{b_1, b_2, \ldots, b_m\}$ of A of size m, then there exists $g \in G$ with $a_i g = b_i$. If $m \geq 2$ then m-transitivity implies $(m-1)$-transitivity.

PROPOSITION 3.5. Let $|A| = n$. Then Sym A is n-transitive and Alt A is $(n-2)$- but not $(n-1)$-transitive.

Proof. Obviously Sym A is n-transitive. Given $\{a_1, \ldots, a_{n-2}\}$ and $\{b_1, \ldots, b_{n-2}\}$. Then precisely one of

$$\begin{pmatrix} a_1 & \cdots & a_{n-2} & a_{n-1} & a_n \\ b_1 & \cdots & b_{n-2} & b_{n-1} & b_n \end{pmatrix} \quad \text{or} \quad \begin{pmatrix} a_1 & \cdots & a_{n-2} & a_{n-1} & a_n \\ b_1 & \cdots & b_{n-2} & b_n & b_{n-1} \end{pmatrix}$$

is even. Here $a_{n-1}, a_n, b_{n-1}, b_n$ are the obvious remaining elements. Thus Alt A is $(n-2)$-transitive but not $(n-1)$-transitive.

PROPOSITION 3.6. Let G be a transitive permutation group on set A. If $m \geq 2$, then G is m-transitive if and only if G_a is (m-1)-transitive on $A - \{a\}$.

<u>Proof</u>. Obviously if G is m-transitive, then G_a is (m-1)-transitive on $A - \{a\}$. Now let G be transitive and let G_a be (m-1)-transitive on $A - \{a\}$. Note since G is transitive this holds for all $a \in A$. Given any two ordered subsets $\{a_1, \ldots, a_m\}$, $\{b_1, \ldots, b_m\}$ choose $g \in G$ with $a_1 g = b_1$. Now choose $h \in G_{b_1}$ with $(a_i g)h = b_i$ for $i = 2, \ldots, m$. Then for $i = 1, 2, \ldots, m$ we have $a_i(gh) = b_i$ since $a_1 g = b_1$ and $h \in G_{b_1}$.

We now obtain a few simple facts about doubly transitive groups.

PROPOSITION 3.7. Let G be transitive. Then G is doubly transitive if and only if for all $g \in G - G_a$ we have $G = G_a \cup G_a g G_a$.

<u>Proof</u>. Suppose G is doubly transitive. Given $g \in G - G_a$. If $h \in G - G_a$ then $ah = b$ and $ag = c$ with $b, c \neq a$. Since G_a is transitive on $A - \{a\}$ we can find $k \in G_a$ with

$bk = c$. Hence $ahk = bk = c = ag$ and $hkg^{-1} \in G_a$ so $h \in G_a g G_a$.

Now let $G = G_a \cup G_a g G_a$. Given $b, c \in A - \{a\}$, then since G is transitive we can find $h_1, h_2 \in G$ with $ah_1 = b$, $ah_2 = c$. Clearly $h_1, h_2 \notin G_a$ so we must have $h_2 = k_1 h_1 k_2$ for some $k_1, k_2 \in G_a$. Then $c = ah_2 = ak_1 h_1 k_2 = ah_1 k_2 = bk_2$ so G_a is transitive on $A - \{a\}$.

Since the above subgroups are obviously maximal we have

PROPOSITION 3.8. If G is doubly transitive, then G is primitive.

PROPOSITION 3.9. Let G be transitive and let G_a have s orbits on A. Then $\sum \theta(g)^2 = s\,|G|$. In particular G is doubly transitive if and only if $\sum \theta(g)^2 = 2\,|G|$.

<u>Proof</u>. Let $\underline{S} = \{(g, a, b) \mid g \in G,\ a, b \in A,\ g \in G_a \cap G_b\}$. We compute the size of $\underline{S}$. For each g the number of ordered pairs (a, b) with $(g, a, b) \in \underline{S}$ is clearly $\theta(g)^2$.

Thus $|\underline{S}| = \sum \theta(g)^2$. Now since G is transitive we see that for some fixed a we have $|\underline{S}| = |A|\,|\underline{T}|$ where $\underline{T} = \{(g, b) \mid g \in G_a,\ b \in A,\ bg = b\}$. As in the proof of Proposition 3.1, $|\underline{T}| = |G_a|\,s$. Hence

$$\sum \theta(g)^2 = |\underline{S}| = [G:G_a]\,|G_a|\,s = |G|\,s$$

and the result follows.

4. NORMAL SUBGROUPS

We study now normal subgroups of transitive groups. The relationship of our first result to this will be apparent later.

PROPOSITION 4.1. Let N be a finite group and let G be a group of automorphisms of N. Then G acts as a permutation group on $N^{\#} = N - \{1\}$.

i. If G is transitive then N is an elementary abelian p-group for some prime p.

ii. If G is doubly transitive then either $|N| = 3$

or N is an elementary abelian 2-group.

iii. If G is triply transitive then $|N| = 4$.

iv. G cannot be quadruply transitive.

Proof. Let $p \mid |N|$. Since G is transitive every nonidentity element of N has order p and hence N is a p-group. Since G must fix $\mathfrak{Z}(N)$ setwise and $\mathfrak{Z}(N) \neq \langle 1 \rangle$, it follows that $N = \mathfrak{Z}(N)$ and (i) holds.

Let G act doubly transitive and suppose $p > 2$. Let $x \in N^{\#}$ so that $x \neq x^{-1}$. If $g \in G$ is such that $xg = x$ then certainly $x^{-1}g = x^{-1}$. Thus x^{-1} must be the only other nonidentity element of N and $|N| = 3$. This yields (ii).

Let G be triply transitive so that $|N| \geq 4$. Clearly G cannot map three elements contained in a subgroup of order 4 to three elements which are not. Hence $|N| = 4$. Since this group has only three nonidentity elements, G cannot be quadruply transitive. This completes the proof.

The more difficult problem of which groups admit 1/2-transitive automorphism groups will be considered later. A normal subgroup N of a permutation group G which is regular is called a regular normal subgroup.

PROPOSITION 4.2. Let G be a permutation group on set A and let N be a regular normal subgroup. If $a \in A$, then the permutation representation of G_a on $A-\{a\}$ and the permutation representation of G_a on $N-\{1\}$ induced by conjugation are the same.

<u>Proof</u>. Since N is regular, there is a one to one correspondence between the elements of $A-\{a\}$ and those of $N^{\#}$ given by $b \leftrightarrow x$, where $b \in A-\{a\}$, $x \in N^{\#}$, if and only if $b = ax$. Since for $g \in G_a$, $g^{-1}xg = x^g \in N$ and $ax^g = ag^{-1}xg = axg = bg$ we see that $b \leftrightarrow x$ implies that $bg \leftrightarrow x^g$ and the result follows.

If G is m-transitive on A and $m > 1$, then G_a is $(m-1)$-transitive on $A-\{a\}$. Hence combining Propositions 4.1 and 4.2 yields

PROPOSITION 4.3. Let G be an m-transitive permutation group of degree n which has a regular normal subgroup N.

i. If $m = 2$, then $n = |N| = p^k$ for some prime p.

ii. If $m = 3$, then either $n = 3$ or $n = 2^k$.

iii. If $m = 4$, then $n = 4$.

iv. We cannot have $m \geq 5$.

We now discuss some applications.

PROPOSITION 4.4. Let G be a transitive permutation group and let $N \triangle G$. Then N is $1/2$-transitive. If further $N \neq \langle 1 \rangle$ and G is primitive, then N is transitive.

Proof. Let B be an orbit of N of minimal length. If $g \in G$ then $(Bg)N = B(gN) = B(Ng) = (BN)g = Bg$ so Bg is a union of orbits of N. By minimality of $|B|$ we see that Bg is an orbit. Since orbits are either disjoint or identical we see that B is a subset of imprimitivity for G. This also shows that every orbit of N is of the form Bg and hence N is $1/2$-transitive. If G is primitive and N is not transitive then $|B| = 1$ and so $N = \langle 1 \rangle$.

PROPOSITION 4.5. Let G be a primitive permutation group having no regular normal subgroups. If G_a is simple, then G is simple.

Proof. Let $N \triangle G$ with $N \neq \langle 1 \rangle$. Since G is primitive, N is transitive. Now G_a is simple and $N_a = (N \cap G_a) \triangle G_a$. Hence either $N_a = \langle 1 \rangle$ or G_a. If $N_a = \langle 1 \rangle$, then N is a regular normal subgroup of G, a contradiction. Thus $N_a = G_a$ and since N is transitive $[N:N_a] = [G:G_a] = |A|$. Hence $N = G$ is simple.

THEOREM 4.6. If $n \geq 5$ then $\mathrm{Alt}(n)$ is a nonabelian simple group.

Proof. First let $n = 5$. Let $N \triangle \mathrm{Alt}(5)$ with $N \neq \langle 1 \rangle$. Since $\mathrm{Alt}(5)$ is triply transitive it is primitive and hence N is transitive. Thus $[N:N_a] = 5$. Let x be an element of N of order 5 so that $J = \langle x \rangle$ is a Sylow 5-subgroup of N and of $\mathrm{Alt}(5)$ since $|\mathrm{Alt}(5)| = 60$. By suitably relabeling the set being permuted we can assume that $x = (1\ 2\ 3\ 4\ 5)$. Set $y = (1\ 2\ 3)$ so that $x^y = (1\ 4\ 5\ 2\ 3) \notin J$. Thus J^y is another Sylow 5-subgroup of N and so J is not normal in

N. By Sylow's theorem $[N:\mathfrak{N}_N(J)] \equiv 1$ (5) and hence $[N:\mathfrak{N}_N(J)] = 6$ so that $30 \mid |N|$. If $|N| = 30$ then since N has $6\cdot(5-1) = 24$ elements of order 5 it follows that there are only 6 elements of order 1, 2 or 3. Now $|N_a| = 6$ for all a and hence N_a fixes all elements of $\{1,2,3,4,5\}$, a contradiction. Thus $N = \mathrm{Alt}(5)$ and Alt(5) is a nonabelian simple group.

Now let $n \geq 6$ and assume that Alt(n-1) is simple. Since Alt(n) with $n \geq 6$ is 4-transitive of degree > 4, it follows from Proposition 4.3 that Alt(n) has no regular normal subgroup. By Proposition 4.5, since $\mathrm{Alt}(n)_a = \mathrm{Alt}(n-1)$ we see that Alt(n) is simple. The result follows by induction.

THEOREM 4.7. Let $n \geq 5$. Then the only nontrivial normal subgroup of Sym(n) is Alt(n).

Proof. Let $N \vartriangle \mathrm{Sym}(n)$. Since $(N \cap \mathrm{Alt}(n)) \vartriangle \mathrm{Alt}(n)$ we have by the above $N \cap \mathrm{Alt}(n) = \langle 1 \rangle$ or Alt(n). Now $[\mathrm{Sym}(n):\mathrm{Alt}(n)] = 2$ so that if $N \supseteq \mathrm{Alt}(n)$ and $N \neq \mathrm{Sym}(n)$

then $N = \mathrm{Alt}(n)$. If $N \cap \mathrm{Alt}(n) = \langle 1 \rangle$ and $N \neq \langle 1 \rangle$ then $|N| = 2$. Since $\mathrm{Sym}(n)$ is primitive, N is transitive, a contradiction.

We mention now a result on solvable groups.

PROPOSITION 4.8. Let G be a transitive permutation group and let H be a transitive subgroup. Then $G = G_a H = HG_a$.

<u>Proof</u>. Let $g \in G$ and let $ag = b$. Since H is transitive there exists $h \in H$ with $ah = b$ and hence $gh^{-1} \in G_a$. Thus $g \in G_a H$ and $G = G_a H$. By taking inverses $G = HG_a$.

PROPOSITION 4.9. Let G be primitive and suppose G has a normal abelian nonidentity subgroup N. Then N is the unique minimal normal subgroup of G. Moreover $\deg G = |N| = p^k$ for some prime p.

<u>Proof</u>. Since $N \Delta G$ and G is primitive we see

that N is transitive. Since N is abelian, it is regular by Proposition 3.2 and hence $|N| = \deg G$. We show now that N is self-centralizing. If not let $g \notin N$ centralize N. Then $H = \langle g, N \rangle$ is abelian and transitive since $H \supseteq N$. Thus H is also regular and $|H| = \deg G = |N|$, a contradiction. Let $M \triangle G$ with $M \neq \langle 1 \rangle$. Then $(M \cap N) \triangle G$ and $M \cap N$ is abelian. Since N is self-centralizing we cannot have $M \cap N = \langle 1 \rangle$. Thus $M \cap N$ is transitive and $|M \cap N| = \deg G$ so $M \cap N = N$. This shows that $M \supseteq N$ and so N is the unique minimal normal subgroup of G. Since N cannot have proper characteristic subgroups we have $|N| = p^k$ and the result follows.

5. AUTOMORPHISM GROUPS

Given group G, we let $\mathrm{Aut}\, G$ denote the group of automorphisms of G. If $g \in G$, then σ_g defined by $x\sigma_g = x^g = g^{-1}xg$ is the inner automorphism induced by g. If $g, h \in G$ then $\sigma_{gh} = \sigma_g \sigma_h$ so the map $g \to \sigma_g$ is a homomorphism of G. The kernel is clearly $\mathfrak{Z}(G)$, the center of G. We denote the image by Inn G, the group of inner automorphisms of G. If $g \in G$ and $\tau \in \text{Aut } G$ then $\sigma_g \tau = \tau \sigma_{g\tau}$. This yields

PROPOSITION 5.1. Inn G Δ Aut G.

We denote the quotient group (Aut G)/(Inn G) by Out G, the group of outer automorphisms of G. We will discuss the relationship of Inn G to Aut G in more detail later. Now we will consider a special case.

PROPOSITION 5.2. Aut G permutes the conjugacy classes of G.

Proof. Let x be conjugate to y with $y = x^g = x\sigma_g$. If $\tau \in \text{Aut } G$, then $y\tau = x\sigma_g\tau = x\tau\sigma_{g\tau}$ so that $y\tau$ is conjugate to $x\tau$.

Two elements of Sym(n) are said to have the same cycle structure if there is a one to one correspondence between the lengths of their cycles.

LEMMA 5.3. Two elements of Sym(n) are conjugate if and only if they have the same cycle structure. If $x \in \mathrm{Alt}(n)$, then the class of x in Sym(n) is either a class of Alt(n) or a union of two classes of Alt(n) of the same size. The former occurs if and only if $\mathcal{L}(x) \not\subseteq \mathrm{Alt}(n)$.

Proof. Let $x \in \mathrm{Sym}(n)$ with $x = (a\ b\ c\ \dots)\ \dots$ and let $y = \begin{pmatrix} a & b & c & \dots \\ a_1 & b_1 & c_1 & \dots \end{pmatrix}$. Then

$$y^{-1}xy = \begin{pmatrix} a_1 & b_1 & c_1 & \dots \\ a & b & c & \dots \end{pmatrix} (a\ b\ c\ \dots)\ \dots \begin{pmatrix} a & b & c & \dots \\ a_1 & b_1 & c_1 & \dots \end{pmatrix}$$

$$= (a_1\ b_1\ c_1\ \dots)\ \dots$$

Thus we see that any two elements of Sym(n) are conjugate if and only if they have the same cycle structure.

Now let $x \in \mathrm{Alt}(n)$ and let y be a fixed element of Sym(n)-Alt(n). Since $\mathrm{Sym}(n) = \mathrm{Alt}(n) \cup y\,\mathrm{Alt}(n)$ we see that every conjugate of x in Sym(n) is a conjugate of either x or x^y in Alt(n). It is easy to see that these two not necessarily distinct classes have the same size. If y can be chosen in $\mathcal{L}(x)$ then there is only one class. If there is only one class then there exists $g \in \mathrm{Alt}(n)$ with $x^g = x^y$ and hence $yg^{-1} \in \mathcal{L}(x)\text{-}\mathrm{Alt}(n)$.

Let T denote the set of 3-cycles in $\mathrm{Sym}(n)$.

LEMMA 5.4. If $n \geq 3$ then $\mathrm{Alt}(n)$ is generated by the elements of T. These form one class if $n \geq 5$ and two classes for $n = 3, 4$.

Proof. Every element of $\mathrm{Alt}(n)$ is a product of an even number of transpositions. We have $(a\ b)(c\ d) = (a\ b\ d)$ if $a = c$, $b \neq d$ and $(a\ b)(c\ d) = (a\ b\ c)(a\ d\ c)$ if a, b, c, d are distinct. Thus the first result follows.

By the above T is a class in $\mathrm{Sym}(n)$. If $n \geq 5$ then $x = (1\ 2\ 3)$ is centralized by $y = (4\ 5) \notin \mathrm{Alt}(n)$ and thus T is a class of $\mathrm{Alt}(n)$. The cases $n = 3$ and 4 are easily checked.

LEMMA 5.5. Let $n \geq 5$ and let γ be an automorphism of $\mathrm{Alt}(n)$ with $T\gamma = T$. Then there exists $g \in \mathrm{Sym}(n)$ with $\gamma = \sigma_g \mid \mathrm{Alt}(n)$.

Proof. We let $o(x)$ denote the order of element x. We have

$$o(\ (1\ 2\ 3)(4\ 5\ 6)\ ) = 3 \qquad o(\ (1\ 2\ 3)(1\ 4\ 5)\ ) = 5$$

$$o(\ (1\ 2\ 3)(1\ 2\ 4)\ ) = 2 \qquad o(\ (1\ 2\ 3)(1\ 4\ 2)\ ) = 3$$

$$o(\ (1\ 2\ 3)(1\ 3\ 2)\ ) = 1.$$

For each $a \neq b$ set $T(a,b) = \{(a\ b\ c) \mid \text{all } c \neq a,b\}$. By the above we see that $T(a,b)$ is a maximal subset of T with the following property.

(*) If x,y are distinct elements of the subset then $o(xy) = 2$.

Conversely let X be a maximal subset of T with property (*). Say $(1\ 2\ 3) \in X$. Since $\{(1\ 2\ 3)\}$ is not maximal, X must contain another element. From the above we can assume this new element looks like $(1\ 2\ 4)$, $(2\ 3\ 4)$ or $(3\ 1\ 4)$, say $(1\ 2\ 4)$. Clearly every other element of X is then of the form $(1\ 2\ c)$ and from the maximality of X, $X = T(1,2)$. Since τ is an automorphism it follows that $T(a,b)\tau = T(a',b')$ for suitable a',b'.

Now set $S(a) = \{(a\ b\ c) \mid \text{all } b,c \text{ with } a,b,c \text{ distinct}\}$.

We show that $S = S(a)$ satisfies the following two conditions.

(**) S is a union of at least eight $T(b,c)$.

(***) If $T(b,c)$ and $T(b',c')$ are disjoint subsets of S then there exists $x \in T(b,c)$ with $x^{-1} \in T(b',c')$.

First $S(a) = \bigcup\{T(a,b) \cup T(b,a) \mid b \neq a\}$ and since $n \geq 5$ (**) holds. If $T(b,c) \subseteq S(a)$ then since $n \geq 4$ we must have either $b = a$ or $c = a$. Thus in (***) there are several possibilities. We can assume that either $b \neq b'$ or $c \neq c'$.

(i) $b = b' = a$, $c \neq c'$. Then $x = (a\ c\ c') \in T(a,c)$ and $x^{-1} = (a\ c'\ c) \in T(a,c')$.

(ii) $c = c' = a$, $b \neq b'$. Then $x = (b\ a\ b') \in T(b,a)$ and $x^{-1} = (b'\ a\ b) \in T(b',a)$.

(iii) $b = c' = a$, $b' = c$. Then $x = (a\ c\ d) \in T(a,c)$ and $x^{-1} = (c\ a\ d) \in T(c,a)$ where $d \neq a, c$.

(iv) $b = c' = a$, $b' \neq c$. Then $x = (a\ c\ b') \in T(a,c)$ and $x \in T(b',a)$.

Conversely let S be any subset satisfying (**) and (***). By (***) any two subsets $T(b,c)$ and $T(b',c')$ must have at least one entry in common. If not all have an entry in common then say S contains $T(1,2)$ or $T(2,1)$, $T(1,3)$ or $T(3,1)$ and $T(2,3)$ or $T(3,2)$. Since S contains at least eight $T(b,c)$ and any other $T(b,c)$ must have an entry in common with all of the preceeding, we have a contradiction. Hence for some a, $S \subseteq S(a)$. Therefore the maximal subsets with (**) and (***) are precisely the $S(a)$.

Since $T(a,b)\tau = T(a'', b'')$ it follows that $S(a)\tau = S(a')$. The function $a \longrightarrow a'$ is one to one since τ^{-1} is an automorphism and hence there exists $g \in \mathrm{Sym}(n)$ with $ag = a'$. Now $(a\ b\ c)\tau \in (\ S(a) \cap S(b) \cap S(c)\ )\tau \subseteq S(a') \cap S(b') \cap S(c')$ and thus $(a\ b\ c)\tau = (a'\ b'\ c')$ or $(a'\ c'\ b')$. Let $(a\ b\ c)\tau = (a'\ c'\ b')$. If $(a\ b\ d)\tau = (a'\ b'\ d')$ then $o(\ (a\ b\ c)(a\ b\ d)\ ) = 2$ while $o(\ (a'\ c'\ b')(a'\ b'\ d')\ ) = 3$, a contradiction. Hence $T(a,b)\tau = T(b', a')$. Since $T(b,a) = T(a,b)^{-1}$ we also have $T(b,a)\tau = T(a', b')$ and thus $[(a\ c\ b)(a\ b\ d)(a\ b\ c)]\tau = (a'\ b'\ c')(a'\ d'\ b')(a'\ c'\ b')$ or $(b\ c\ d)\tau = (a'\ c'\ d')$, a contradiction.

This shows that when restricted to T we have $\tau = \sigma_g$. Since T generates Alt(n) this yields finally $\tau = \sigma_g | \mathrm{Alt}(n)$.

LEMMA 5.6. If $\tau \in \mathrm{Aut}(\mathrm{Alt}(n))$, $n > 3$ and $n \neq 6$ then $T\tau = T$.

Proof. If $n = 4$ or 5 then T is the set of all elements of $\mathrm{Alt}(n)$ of order 3 so of course $T\tau = T$. Let $n > 6$. Then T is a conjugacy class of $\mathrm{Alt}(n)$ with the property that

(*) If $x \in T$, then $o(x) = 3$.

(**) If $x, y \in T$, then $o(xy) \leq 5$.

Conversely let S be a conjugacy class satisfying the above two conditions. Then every element of S has the same cycle structure and by (*) they are products of r 3-cycles and s 1-cycles. If $S \neq T$, then $r \geq 2$. If $s > 0$ then

$$x = (1\ 2\ 3)(4\ 5\ 6)(7)\ldots \in S$$

$$y = (1\ 2\ 4)(3\ 5\ 7)(6)\ldots \in S$$

$$xy = (1\ 4\ 7\ 3\ 2\ 5\ 6)\ldots$$

which contradicts (**). If $s = 0$, then $n > 6$ yields $n \geq 9$ and

$$x = (1\ 2\ 3)(4\ 5\ 6)(7\ 8\ 9)\ldots \in S$$

$$y = (1\ 2\ 4)(3\ 5\ 7)(6\ 8\ 9)\ldots \in S$$

$$xy = (1\ 4\ 7\ 9\ 3\ 2\ 5\ 8\ 6)\ldots$$

again a contradiction. Thus $S = T$ and clearly $T\tau = T$.

If $n > 3$ then certainly $\mathcal{L}_{\mathrm{Sym}(n)}(\mathrm{Alt}(n)) = \langle 1 \rangle$. Thus there is a monomorphism $\mathrm{Sym}(n) \to \mathrm{Aut}(\mathrm{Alt}(n))$ given by $g \in \mathrm{Sym}(n) \longrightarrow \sigma_g | \mathrm{Alt}(n)$. In this way we say that $\mathrm{Sym}(n) \subseteq \mathrm{Aut}(\mathrm{Alt}(n))$.

THEOREM 5.7. If $n > 3$ and $n \neq 6$ then $\mathrm{Aut}(\mathrm{Alt}(n)) = \mathrm{Sym}(n)$. If $n = 6$ then $[\mathrm{Aut}(\mathrm{Alt}(n)) : \mathrm{Sym}(n)] = 2$.

Proof. First let $n = 4$ and let u and v be elements of $\mathrm{Alt}(4)$ of order 2 and 3 respectively. It is easy to see that u and v generate $\mathrm{Alt}(4)$ so an automorphism is uniquely determined by its effect on u and v. Now $\mathrm{Alt}(4)$ has three elements of order 2 and eight of order 3. Thus $|\mathrm{Aut}(\mathrm{Alt}(4))| \leq 3 \cdot 8 = |\mathrm{Sym}(4)|$ and the $n = 4$ result holds.

Now let $n \geq 5$ but $n \neq 6$. The result follows here by Lemmas 5.5 and 5.6. Finally let $n = 6$. Then $\mathrm{Alt}(6)$ has two classes of elements of order 3, namely $T = \{(a\ b\ c)\}$

and $S = \{(a\ b\ c)(d\ e\ f)\}$. Note that S is a class since the odd permutation $(a\ d)(b\ e)(c\ f)$ centralizes one of its members. If $\tau \in \mathrm{Aut}(\mathrm{Alt}(6))$ then either $T\tau = T$ or $T\tau = S$. If L is the subgroup of $\mathrm{Aut}(\mathrm{Alt}(6))$ with $T\tau = T$ then certainly this subgroup has index 1 or 2. By Lemma 5.5 this yields $[\mathrm{Aut}(\mathrm{Alt}(6)):\mathrm{Sym}(6)] = 1$ or 2.

We show that this index is 2 by first constructing an outer (that is, not inner) automorphism of $G = \mathrm{Sym}(6)$. Let $H = G_a$, the subgroup fixing a point a. Then $[G:H] = 6$. Now consider Sym(5). This group contains six Sylow 5-subgroups which Sym(5) permutes transitively by conjugation. Since Alt(5) is the unique proper normal subgroup of Sym(5) we see that this representation is faithful. Thus we embed Sym(5) isomorphically in Sym(6). Let K be this subgroup of $G = \mathrm{Sym}(6)$. Then $[G:K] = 6$ but $K \neq G_b$ for any b since Sym(5) does not have a normal Sylow 5-subgroup. Let $\{x_i\}$ be a set of right coset representatives of H and let $\{y_i\}$ be a set for K. Now G permutes the right cosets of H and of K by

$$\alpha : g \longrightarrow \begin{pmatrix} Hx_1 & Hx_2 & \ldots & Hx_6 \\ Hx_1 g & Hx_2 g & \ldots & Hx_6 g \end{pmatrix}.$$

$$\beta : g \longrightarrow \begin{pmatrix} Kx_1 & Kx_2 & \ldots & Kx_6 \\ Kx_1 g & Kx_2 g & \ldots & Kx_6 g \end{pmatrix}.$$

Clearly α and β are isomorphisms. Thus we have

$$\begin{array}{ccc} G & \xrightarrow{\alpha} & \mathrm{Sym}\,\{Hx_i\} \\ & & \downarrow \gamma \\ G & \xrightarrow{\beta} & \mathrm{Sym}\,\{Ky_i\} \end{array}$$

where γ is induced by the correspondence $Hx_i \longleftrightarrow Ky_i$. Then $\tau = \alpha\gamma\beta^{-1}$ is an automorphism of G. If $x_1 = y_1 = 1$, then $H\tau = K$ and hence τ is not an inner automorphism since H is not conjugate to K.

Now Alt(6) is characteristic in G so $\tau\,|\,\mathrm{Alt}(6)$ is an automorphism. If $\tau\,|\,\mathrm{Alt}(6) = \sigma_g\,|\,\mathrm{Alt}(6)$ for some $g \in G$ then $(H \cap \mathrm{Alt}(6))^g = (K \cap \mathrm{Alt}(6))$. This says that some Sylow 5-subgroup of Sym(5) is normal in Alt(5), a contradiction. This completes the proof.

We see that for $n \geq 5$, Out (Alt(n)) has order 2 or 4 and hence is abelian. It has been conjectured by O. Schreier that the outer automorphism group of every simple group is solvable. This has been verified for all the known simple groups.

We now find the automorphism group of Sym(n).

LEMMA 5.8. Let G be a group with $\mathfrak{Z}(G) = \langle 1 \rangle$. Then $\mathfrak{C}_{\text{Aut } G}(\text{Inn } G) = \langle 1 \rangle$.

<u>Proof.</u> Let $\tau \in \text{Aut } G$ centralize $\text{Inn } G$. Then for all $x \in G$, $\sigma_x \tau = \tau \sigma_{x\tau} = \tau \sigma_x$. Hence $\sigma_{x\tau} = \sigma_x$ and since $\mathfrak{Z}(G) = \langle 1 \rangle$ we have $x\tau = x$.

The above show that if $\mathfrak{Z}(G) = \langle 1 \rangle$ then $\mathfrak{Z}(\text{Aut } G) = \langle 1 \rangle$. Let $H \triangle \text{Aut } G$ with $\text{Inn } G \subseteq H$. There is a homomorphism of $\text{Aut } G$ into $\text{Aut } H$ given by the restriction of the inner automorphisms of $\text{Aut } G$ to H. Since $H \supseteq \text{Inn } G$ and $\mathfrak{C}_{\text{Aut } G}(\text{Inn } G) = \langle 1 \rangle$ it follows that this homomorphism is one to one and hence we can say $\text{Aut } H \supseteq \text{Aut } G$.

THEOREM 5.9. Let $\mathfrak{Z}(G) = \langle 1 \rangle$ and let $H \triangle \text{Aut } G$ with $\text{Inn } G \subseteq H$. Suppose further that $\text{Inn } G$ is characteristic in H. Then $\text{Aut } H = \text{Aut } G$.

Proof. Let T be an automorphism of H. Since $\operatorname{Inn} G$ is characteristic in H we see that $T \mid \operatorname{Inn} G$ is an automorphism of $\operatorname{Inn} G$. Define τ by $\sigma_x T = \sigma_{x\tau}$ for $x \in G$. Note τ is well defined since $\mathfrak{z}(G) = \langle 1 \rangle$. Since T is an automorphism we have for $g, h \in G$

$$\sigma_{(gh)\tau} = \sigma_{gh} T = (\sigma_g \sigma_h) T = (\sigma_g T)(\sigma_h T)$$
$$= \sigma_{g\tau} \sigma_{h\tau} = \sigma_{(g\tau)(h\tau)}$$

so $(gh)\tau = (g\tau)(h\tau)$. Since τ is clearly one to one we have $\tau \in \operatorname{Aut} G$. Let S_τ denote the restriction to H of the inner automorphism of $\operatorname{Aut} G$ induced by τ. This exists since $H \triangle \operatorname{Aut} G$.

Now $\tau^{-1}\sigma_x\tau = \sigma_{x\tau}$ so $S_\tau \mid \operatorname{Inn} G = T \mid \operatorname{Inn} G$. Let $V = T^{-1}S_\tau$ so that V is an automorphism of H with $V \mid \operatorname{Inn} G = 1$. Let $\alpha \in H$. If $x \in G$ then since $\alpha^{-1}\sigma_x\alpha$ belongs to $\operatorname{Inn} G$ we have

$$\alpha^{-1}\sigma_x\alpha = (\alpha^{-1}\sigma_x\alpha)V = (\alpha V)^{-1}(\sigma_x V)(\alpha V) = (\alpha V)^{-1}\sigma_x(\alpha V)$$

and hence $(\alpha V)\alpha^{-1} \in \mathcal{L}_{\operatorname{Aut} G}(\operatorname{Inn} G) = \langle 1 \rangle$. Thus $\alpha V = \alpha$ and $V = 1$. Therefore $T = S_\tau$ and the result follows.

COROLLARY 5.10. If $n > 3$, $n \neq 6$ then Aut (Sym(n)) is equal to Sym(n) and if $n = 6$ then $[\mathrm{Aut}\,(\mathrm{Sym}(n)) : \mathrm{Sym}(n)] = 2$.

Proof. In Sym(n) the transpositions (1 2) and (1 3) are conjugate. Hence $(1\ 2\ 3) = (1\ 2)(1\ 3)$ is an element of the commutator subgroup Sym(n)'. Since Alt(n) is generated by all 3-cycles we see that Alt(n) = Sym(n)'. Hence Sym(n) has a unique subgroup of index 2. Let G = Alt(n). With $n > 3$, $\mathfrak{z}(G) = \langle 1 \rangle$ and by the above Inn G is characteristic in Sym(n). By Theorems 5.7 and 5.9 Aut (Sym(n)) ≈ Aut (Alt(n)) and the result follows.

A group G with $\mathfrak{z}(G) = \langle 1 \rangle$ and Inn G = Aut G is called complete. By the above Sym(n) is complete if $n > 3$ and $n \neq 6$.

THEOREM 5.11. If G is a nonabelian simple group then Inn G is characteristic in Aut G and hence Aut G is complete.

Proof. Let $N \triangleleft \mathrm{Aut}\, G$ with $N \nsupseteq \mathrm{Inn}\, G$. Then

$(N \cap \text{Inn } G) \Delta \text{Inn } G$ and since the latter group is simple, $N \cap \text{Inn } G = \langle 1 \rangle$. Now $\text{Inn } G \Delta \text{Aut } G$ so we see that $N \subseteq \mathcal{L}_{\text{Aut } G}(\text{Inn } G) = \langle 1 \rangle$. Hence Inn G is the unique minimal normal subgroup of Aut G. The result now follows from Theorem 5.9.

6. SUBNORMAL SUBGROUPS

The preceeding theorem states that every nonabelian simple group is a normal subgroup of a complete group. In this section we will extend this result.

A group is semisimple if it is a direct product of nonabelian simple groups.

LEMMA 6.1. Let $G = \prod K_i$ be semisimple. If $N \Delta G$ then N is a product of some of the K_i.

<u>Proof</u>. Say N is a subdirect product of $K_1, \ldots, K_r$. Let $x \in N$ project nontrivially on K_1. Then we can find $y \in K_1$ with $(x, y) \in K_1 \cap N$ and $(x, y) \neq 1$. Since

$(K_1 \cap N) \triangle K_1$ we have $K_1 \cap N = K_1$ and $N \supseteq K_1$. Thus $N = \prod_1^r K_i$.

LEMMA 6.2. Let $N \subseteq G \subseteq H$ with $N, G \triangle H$. If G is semisimple then there exists $M \triangle H$ with $G = N \times M$.

Proof. Say $G = K_1 \times \ldots \times K_n$ and by the above assume that $N = K_1 \times \ldots \times K_r$. If $h \in H$ then $K_i^h \triangle G$ and hence $K_i^h = K_{i'}$ for some i'. Hence H permutes the K_i. Since $N \triangle H$, $\{K_1, \ldots, K_r\}$ is a union of orbits and so $\{K_{r+1}, \ldots, K_n\}$ is a union of orbits. Thus $M = K_{r+1} \times \ldots \times K_n \triangle H$ and the result follows.

LEMMA 6.3. Let $G_1, G_2 \triangle H$ and suppose both G_i are semisimple. Then so is $G_1 G_2$.

Proof. $N = G_1 \cap G_2 \triangle H$ and hence by the above we have $G_1 = N \times M_1$, $G_2 = N \times M_2$ with $M_i \triangle H$. Then $G_1 G_2 = N M_1 M_2 \cong N \times M_1 \times M_2$ is clearly semisimple.

We mention now where these groups come into play.

PROPOSITION 6.4. Let G be a minimal normal subgroup of H. Then either G is a p-group for some prime p or G is semisimple.

Proof. Let K be a minimal normal subgroup of G. Then clearly G is generated by all K^h, $h \in H$ and these form a set of isomorphic minimal normal subgroups of G. It is easy to see that a suitable subset of these will direct product to G. Say $G = K_1 \times K_2 \times \ldots \times K_n$ where $K_i = K^{h_i}$. If $N \triangle K_i$ then clearly $N \triangle G$. Thus since K_i is minimal normal in G, it is simple. If K_i is nonabelian and simple, then G is semisimple. If K_i is a p-group, then G is a p-group.

A subgroup G of H is subnormal, written $G \triangle\triangle H$, if there exists a chain $G = L_0 < L_1 < \ldots < L_m = H$ with $L_i \triangle L_{i+1}$. Here m is the length of the chain and $m(G, H)$ is the length of the minimal such chain.

THEOREM 6.5. (Wielandt) The subnormal subgroups of H form a sublattice of the lattice of all subgroups.

<u>Proof</u>. Let $U, V \Delta\Delta H$ and let $U = U_0 < U_1 < \ldots < U_m = H$, $V = V_0 < V_1 < \ldots < V_n = H$ be appropriate subnormal series with $m = m(U,H)$, $n = m(V,H)$. Then

$$\begin{aligned} U \cap V = U_0 \cap V_0 \subseteq U_0 \cap V_1 \subseteq \ldots \subseteq U_0 \cap V_n \\ = U_0 < U_1 < \ldots < U_m = H \end{aligned}$$

is a subnormal series. Hence $U \cap V \Delta\Delta H$.

We show that $\langle U, V\rangle \Delta\Delta H$ by induction on $[H:U]$. Suppose first that $U \Delta H$. Then $\langle U, V_i\rangle = UV_i$ and hence $UV = UV_0 \subseteq UV_1 \subseteq \ldots \subseteq UV_n = H$ is a subnormal series and $\langle U, V\rangle \Delta\Delta H$. Now by induction $K = \langle U_1, V\rangle \Delta\Delta H$. If $K \neq H$, then since $U \Delta\Delta K$, $V \Delta\Delta K$ and $[K:U] < [H:U]$ we have $\langle U, V\rangle \Delta\Delta K$. Thus $\langle U, V\rangle \Delta\Delta H$. Hence we can assume that $\langle U_1, V\rangle = H$ and $U \not\Delta H$. Since $\eta(U) \supseteq U_1$, the latter implies that $\eta(U) \not\supseteq V$. Choose $v \in V$ with $U^v \neq U$. Now $U^v = U_0{}^v < U_1{}^v < \ldots < U_{m-1}{}^v = U_{m-1}$ shows that $U^v \Delta\Delta U_{m-1}$. Since $[U_{m-1}:U] < [H:U]$ we see that $\langle U, U^v\rangle \Delta\Delta U_{m-1}$ and hence $\langle U, U^v\rangle \Delta\Delta H$. But $[H:\langle U, U^v\rangle] < [H:U]$ so $\langle U, U^v, V\rangle = \langle U, V\rangle \Delta\Delta H$ and the result follows.

A property $\underline{P}$ of groups is called normally persistent if: (1) every group isomorphic to a group with property $\underline{P}$

also has property $\underline{P}$; and (2) in a given group the subgroup generated by a collection of normal subgroups having property $\underline{P}$ also has property $\underline{P}$.

Examples of normally persistent properties are being a p-group for a fixed prime p or being semisimple. Replacing the word "normal" by "subnormal" in the above yields a definition of subnormally persistent properties.

THEOREM 6.6. (Wielandt) Normal persistence implies subnormal persistence.

Proof. We call groups with property $\underline{P}$, $\underline{P}$-groups. Let $\underline{P}$ be a normally persistent property. Let $\{U_i\}$ be a set of subnormal $\underline{P}$-subgroups of H. We show that $K = \langle U_i \rangle$ is a $\underline{P}$-group by induction on $\max m(U_i, H)$. Let X be one of these groups U_i and let $X = X_0 < X_1 < \ldots < X_m = H$ be a subnormal series of minimal length. If $k \in K$ then since $X_{m-1} \Delta H$ we have $X^k = X_0{}^k < X_1{}^k < \ldots < X_{m-1} < H$. Thus $m(X^k, X_{m-1}) < m(X, H)$. By induction $X^K = \langle X^k \mid \text{all } k \in K \rangle$ is a $\underline{P}$-group. Hence

$U_1^K, U_2^K, \ldots$ are $\underline{P}$-groups normal in K. Since $\underline{P}$ is normally persistent $U_1^K U_2^K \ldots$ is a $\underline{P}$-subgroup of K. Now $K = \langle U_i \rangle$ so $K = U_1^K U_2^K \ldots$ is a $\underline{P}$-group and the result follows.

COROLLARY 6.7. The properties of being a p-group for a fixed prime p or of being semisimple are subnormally persistent.

PROPOSITION 6.8. Let $G \Delta\Delta H$. Then there exists chains $\langle 1 \rangle = B_0 < B_1 < \ldots < B_r = G$ and $\langle 1 \rangle = H_0 < H_1 < \ldots < H_r \subseteq H$ with $B_i \Delta G$, $H_i \Delta H$, B_{i+1}/B_i is either a p_{i+1}-group or semisimple, $H_i = B_i^H$ and $H_i \cap G = B_i$. Moreover B_{i+1}/B_i and H_{i+1}/H_i are either p_{i+1}-groups and there is a normal subgroup U_{i+1} of G with a p_{i+1}-factor group or B_{i+1}/B_i and H_{i+1}/H_i are semisimple in which case set $U_{i+1} = G$. Then $(U_{i+1}, H_{i+1}) \subseteq (U_{i+1} \cap H_{i+1})H_i \subseteq B_{i+1}H_i$.

<u>Proof</u>. If $G = \langle 1 \rangle$ then set $B_0 = \langle 1 \rangle$. If $G \neq \langle 1 \rangle$, then a minimal normal subgroup of G is either a p_1-group

or semisimple by Proposition 6.4. In the first case let B_1 be the maximum normal p_1-subgroup of G. In the second case let B_1 be the maximum normal semisimple subgroup of G. Since these properties are normally persistent B_1 exists. Now look at G/B_1 and similarly form B_2/B_1. Continuing this construction we obtain the chain $\langle 1\rangle = B_0 < B_1 < \ldots < B_r = G$ with $B_i \Delta G$. We set $H_i = B_i^H = \langle B_i^h \mid \text{all } h \in H\rangle$ so we have $H_i \Delta H$ and $\langle 1\rangle = H_0 \subseteq H_1 \subseteq \ldots \subseteq H_r \subseteq H$.

Clearly $H_{i+1}/H_i = (B_{i+1}H_i/H_i)^{H_{i+1}/H_i}$. Also $B_{i+1}H_i/H_i$ is a factor group of B_{i+1}/B_i since $H_i \cap B_{i+1} \supseteq B_i$ so by Corollary 6.7, B_{i+1}/B_i and H_{i+1}/H_i are either both p_{i+1}-groups or both semisimple. We show that $H_i \cap G = B_i$ by induction on i. It is clear for $i = 0$. Suppose $H_i \cap G = B_i$. Then $(H_{i+1} \cap G)/B_i$ is a subnormal subgroup of H_{i+1}/H_i. By the maximality of B_{i+1} this yields $B_{i+1} \supseteq H_{i+1} \cap G$. Since clearly $H_{i+1} \cap G \supseteq B_{i+1}$, this fact follows.

It remains to discuss the subgroups U_i. There are two cases to consider. Since we wish to show that $(U_{i+1}, H_{i+1}) \subseteq (U_{i+1} \cap H_{i+1})H_i$ it clearly suffices to work in

H/H_i or in other words we can assume that $i = 0$. Then we want $(U_1, H_1) \subseteq (U_1 \cap H_1)$.

<u>Case 1</u>. B_1 is semisimple. Then H_1 is semisimple and we want $(G, H_1) \subseteq B_1$. Let $C = GH_1$. We show that $G \Delta C$. Since $G \Delta\Delta C$, let $G = G_0 < G_1 < \ldots < G_s = C$ be a subnormal chain of minimal length. We have $H_1 \Delta C$, $G_{s-1} \Delta C$ so $H_1 \cap G_{s-1} \Delta C$. By Lemma 6.2 we have $H_1 = (H_1 \cap G_{s-1}) \times D$ with $D \Delta C$. Then $C = G_{s-1}H_1 = G_{s-1}D = G_{s-1} \times D$. If $s > 1$, then $G_{s-2} \Delta G_{s-1}$ implies that $G_{s-2} \Delta C$, a contradiction. Thus $s = 1$ and $G \Delta GH_1$. Therefore $(G, H_1) \subseteq G \cap H_1 = B_1$ and this result follows.

<u>Case 2</u>. B_1 is a p_1-group. Thus H_1 is a p_1-group. Let $C = GH_1$ and let $U_1 = \bigcap G^x$ where the intersection runs over all $x \in C$. Then $U_1 \Delta C$, $H_1 \Delta C$ so $(U_1, H_1) \subseteq U_1 \cap H_1 \subseteq G \cap H_1 = B_1$. We must show that G/U_1 is a p_1-group. Let Q be a Sylow q-subgroup of G with $q \neq p_1$. Let $G = G_0 < G_1 < \ldots < G_s = C$ be a subnormal series. We show by inverse induction that for all $x \in C$,

$G_i xQ = G_i x$. This is clear for $i = s$. Let us consider $G_i xQ$. By induction $G_{i+1} xQ = G_{i+1} x$. Thus Q permutes the right cosets of G_i contained in $G_{i+1} x$ by right multiplication. Now all orbits have size a power of q. On the other hand since $GH_1 = C$ we see that $[C:G]$ is a power of p_1. Thus Q must fix at least one coset. Say it fixes $G_i yx$ with $y \in G_{i+1}$. Then $G_i yxQ = G_i yx$. Multiplying this on the left by y^{-1} yields since $y \in G_{i+1}$, $G_i xQ = G_i x$. Thus we have $GxQ = Gx$ for all $x \in C$ and hence $xQx^{-1} \subseteq G$. Therefore $Q \subseteq G^x$ and $Q \subseteq U_1$. This shows that G/U_1 is a p_1-group and the proof is complete.

PROPOSITION 6.9. Let G be a subnormal subgroup of H and suppose that $\mathcal{L}_H(G) = \langle 1 \rangle$. Then $|H|$ is bounded by some function of $|G|$.

Proof. Let $\langle 1 \rangle = B_0 < B_1 < \ldots < B_r = G$ and $\langle 1 \rangle = H_0 < H_1 < \ldots < H_r \subseteq H$ be the chains of Proposition 6.8. Assuming we have found an upper bound for $|H_i|$ we will obtain a bound for $|H_{i+1}|$. Since $r \leq |G|$ this will yield a bound for $|H_r|$.

Case 1. B_{i+1}/B_i is semisimple. Then by Proposition 6.8 H_{i+1} normalizes GH_i. Since $\mathcal{C}_H(G) = \langle 1 \rangle$ we see that H_{i+1} is contained isomorphically in Aut (GH_i). Now $|GH_i| \leq |G|\,|H_i|$ so the result follows here.

Case 2. B_{i+1}/B_i is a p_{i+1}-group. Let P^* be a Sylow p_{i+1}-subgroup of G and extend this to P^{**} a Sylow p_{i+1}-subgroup of H. Then since $H_{i+1} \triangle H$, $P = P^{**} \cap H_{i+1}$ is a Sylow p_{i+1}-subgroup of H_{i+1}. Let U_{i+1} be as in Proposition 6.8. Then $G = P^* U_{i+1}$ and $H_{i+1} = PH_i$. Since $|H_{i+1}| \leq |P|\,|H_i|$ it suffices to bound $|P|$. Now P normalizes $U_{i+1}H_i$ and hence if $K = \mathcal{C}_P(U_{i+1}H_i)$ then P/K is contained isomorphically in Aut $(U_{i+1}H_i)$. Thus $|P/K|$ is bounded. We show now that $K = \langle 1 \rangle$. First $K \triangle P$. Also P^* normalizes $P = P^{**} \cap H_{i+1}$ and $U_{i+1}H_i$ and thus P^* normalizes K. Then K is normal in the p_{i+1}-group PP^*. If $K \neq \langle 1 \rangle$ then since PP^* is nilpotent we can find a subgroup J with $J \subseteq K$, $|J| = p_{i+1}$ and $J \triangle PP^*$. We see that PP^* acts on J and since $|J^{\#}| < p_{i+1}$ this shows that

J is central in PP^*. Thus J centralizes P^*. Since $J \subseteq K$, J centralizes U_{i+1} and hence J centralizes $P^*U_{i+1} = G$, a contradiction. Hence $K = \langle 1 \rangle$ and $|P|$ is bounded.

In this way we have bounded $|H_r|$. Now $H_r \Delta H$ and $G \subseteq H_r$. Thus $\mathcal{L}_H(H_r) = \langle 1 \rangle$ and so H is contained isomorphically in Aut H_r. This completes the proof.

Let G be a group with $\mathfrak{z}(G) = \langle 1 \rangle$. Then $G \simeq \text{Inn } G$ and $\text{Inn } G \Delta \text{Aut } G$. Also $\mathcal{L}_{\text{Aut } G}(\text{Inn } G) = \langle 1 \rangle$ so $\mathfrak{z}(\text{Aut } G) = \langle 1 \rangle$. Thus we can take Aut (Aut G) and continue this process. In this way we obtain a subnormal series $G = G_0 \subseteq G_1 \subseteq G_2 \subseteq \ldots$ where $G_{i+1} \simeq \text{Aut } G_i$. This is the automorphism tower of G. The following theorem says that G can be subnormally embedded in a complete group.

THEOREM 6.10. (Wielandt) The automorphism tower of a finite group G with $\mathfrak{z}(G) = \langle 1 \rangle$ is of finite height.

Proof. Let $G = G_0 \subseteq G_1 \subseteq G_2 \subseteq \ldots$ be the automorphism tower of G. If we can show that $\mathcal{L}_{G_i}(G) = \langle 1 \rangle$

then by the previous proposition $|G_i|$ is bounded by some function of $|G|$. Hence the result will follow.

We show in fact by induction on $k \geq 1$, that $\mathcal{L}_{G_j}(G_i) = \langle 1 \rangle$ where $j - i = k$. If $k = 1$ the result holds by Lemma 5.8. Assume the result holds for k and let $j - i = k+1$. By induction $\mathcal{L}_{G_{j-1}}(G_i) = \langle 1 \rangle$. Let $A = \mathcal{N}_{G_{j-1}}(G_i)$ so that $A \supseteq G_{i+1}$. Now since $\mathcal{L}_{G_{j-1}}(G_i) = \langle 1 \rangle$, A is embedded isomorphically in $\mathrm{Aut}\, G_i$ a group with $|\mathrm{Aut}\, G_i| = |G_{i+1}|$. Thus $\mathcal{N}_{G_{j-1}}(G_i) = G_{i+1}$ and similarly $\mathcal{N}_{G_j}(G_{i+1}) = G_{i+2}$. Let $b \in \mathcal{L}_{G_j}(G_i)$. Then b normalizes G_{j-1} and G_i and hence b normalizes $\mathcal{N}_{G_{j-1}}(G_i) = G_{i+1}$. Thus $b \in G_{i+2}$. Let $x \in G_{i+1}$ and $y \in G_i$. Then $y, y^x \in G_i$ so $y = y^b$ and $y^x = y^{xb}$. These yield $y^{bxb^{-1}x^{-1}} = y$. Now $bxb^{-1}x^{-1} \in G_{i+1}$ and this element centralizes G_i. Hence by Lemma 5.8, $bxb^{-1}x^{-1} = 1$. Thus b centralizes G_{i+1} and again this yields $b = 1$. The theorem is proved.

7. GROUPS OF PRIME DEGREE

The main result of this section is due to Burnside.

The proof is due to Wielandt.

Let G be a permutation group on set A. Let F be a field and let FA be the set of maps from A into F. If $f \in FA$, $g \in G$ we define f^g by $f^g(a) = f(ag^{-1})$. We have $(f^g)^h(a) = f^g(ah^{-1}) = f(ah^{-1}g^{-1}) = f^{gh}(a)$ so G permutes the elements of FA. Let $\mathrm{Hom}_G(FA, FA)$ denote the set of all homomorphisms from FA to FA which commute with the action of G.

LEMMA 7.1. Let G be transitive on A and suppose G_a has s orbits on A. Then $\dim_F \mathrm{Hom}_G(FA, FA) = s$. Hence G is doubly transitive if and only if $\dim_F \mathrm{Hom}_G(FA, FA) = 2$.

<u>Proof</u>. For $a \in A$ define $f_a \in FA$ by $f_a(a) = 1$, $f_a(b) = 0$ if $b \neq a$. It is clear that the functions f_a form a basis for FA. Moreover $f_a{}^g = f_{ag}$. Hence since G is transitive, an element of $\mathrm{Hom}_G(FA, FA)$ is uniquely determined by the image of f_a for some fixed a. Thus $\dim_F \mathrm{Hom}_G(FA, FA)$ is equal to the number of linearly independent choices for the image of f_a. If $f_a \longrightarrow f$, then

since G_a fixes f_a we must have G_a fixing f. If $f = \sum \alpha_b f_b$ with $\alpha_b \in F$, then G_a fixes f if and only if the coefficients α_b are constant on the orbits of G_a. This clearly yields the result.

LEMMA 7.2. Let $F = GF(p)$, the field with p elements. If f is a function from F to F then there exists a unique polynomial $g \in F[x]$ of degree $\leq p-1$ with $f(\alpha) = g(\alpha)$ for all $\alpha \in F$.

<u>Proof.</u> The system of equations in the unknowns c_i

$$\sum_0^{p-1} c_i \alpha^i = f(\alpha) \qquad \alpha \in F$$

has a nonzero Vandermonde determinant (here $0^0 = 1$) and hence we can uniquely solve for $c_0, \ldots, c_{p-1}$. Clearly $g(x) = \sum c_i x^i$ is the desired polynomial.

THEOREM 7.3. (Burnside) Let G be a transitive permutation group of prime degree p on a set A. Then either G is doubly transitive or we can identify A with

$F = GF(p)$ in such a way that $G \subseteq \{cx+d \mid c, d \in F,\ c \neq 0\}$.

Proof. The result is trivial for $p = 2, 3$ so we assume $p \geq 5$. Since $p = [G:G_a]$, $p \mid |G|$. Let $P = \langle g \rangle$ be a subgroup of G of order p. Clearly g is a p-cycle. We identify A with $F = GF(p)$ in such a way that $g = (p-1\ p-2\ \ldots\ 2\ 1\ 0)$, that is $g: x \rightarrow x-1$.

Now FA is a G-module and thus also a P-module of dimension p. If M is a subspace of FA, then M is P-invariant if and only if $f \in M$ implies $f^g \in M$. By the preceeding lemma FA is the set of all polynomials in $F[x]$ of degree $\leq p-1$. The multiplication (pointwise) in FA is that of $F[x]/(x^p - x)$. Now $f^g(x) = f(xg^{-1}) = f(x+1)$. Thus M is P-invariant if $f \in M$ implies that $\Delta f = f(x+1) - f(x) \in M$.

Suppose $f(x) = c_r x^r + \ldots + c_0 \in M$ with $c_r \neq 0$. Then M contains Δf a polynomial of degree exactly $r-1$ since $r < p$. Thus M contains a polynomial of each degree $\leq r$. Hence since M is a subspace, M contains all polynomials of degree $\leq r$. Set $M_r = \{f \in F[x] \mid \deg f \leq r\}$ for $0 \leq r \leq p-1$ Then M_r is P-invariant and these are the only nonzero P-submodules of FA. All G-submodules lie among these and $\langle 0 \rangle$.

Now $\langle 0 \rangle$, M_0 and $M_{p-1} = FA$ are clearly G-submodules. Also $\{f \in FA \mid \sum_{c \in F} f(c) = 0\}$ is a G-submodule of codimension 1 so this must be M_{p-2}. Suppose for some integer r, $0 \leq r \leq p-3$ we have M_r and M_{r+1} both G-modules. Consider the residual $M_{r+1}:M_r = \{f \in FA \mid fM_r \subseteq M_{r+1}\}$. This is a G-submodule of FA and since $r+2 < p$, $x^2 \notin M_{r+1}:M_r$. Thus $M_1 = M_{r+1}:M_r$ is a G-submodule. For $h \in G$ we have $x^{h^{-1}} = cx+d$ for some $c, d \in F$. Evaluating these functions at $\alpha \in A$ yields $\alpha h = c\alpha + d$ and the result follows.

We now demonstrate the existence of M_r, M_{r+1} as G-modules if G is not doubly transitive. Since G is not doubly transitive, Lemma 7.1 yields $\dim_F \mathrm{Hom}_G(FA, FA) \geq 3$. If $\gamma \in \mathrm{Hom}_G(FA, FA)$ and $f \in FA$ then we have $(\Delta f)\gamma = (f^g - f)\gamma = (f\gamma)^g - (f\gamma) = \Delta(f\gamma)$. Thus if $(FA)\gamma = M_{r+1}$ then $M_{p-2}\gamma = (\Delta M_{p-1})\gamma = \Delta(M_{p-1}\gamma) = \Delta(FA\gamma) = M_r$ and both M_{r+1} and M_r are G-submodules. It therefore suffices to find γ with $(FA)\gamma \neq \langle 0 \rangle$, M_0 or M_{p-1}.

Let $f \in M_{p-1} - M_{p-2}$. Then every element of FA can be obtained from f by applications of Δ and F-linearity.

Since $\Upsilon \in \mathrm{Hom}_G(FA, FA)$ commutes with these operations it follows that $f\Upsilon$ determines Υ. The map $\Upsilon \to f\Upsilon$ is then a faithful linear transformation from $\mathrm{Hom}_G(FA, FA)$ into FA. Since $\dim_F \mathrm{Hom}_G(FA, FA) \geq 3$ we see that the image cannot consist of polynomials of degree only 0 or p-1. Hence if Υ is such that $f\Upsilon$ has degree $r+1 \neq 0, p-1$ then $(FA)\Upsilon = M_{r+1}$ and the proof is complete.

Suppose G is doubly transitive of degree n. Then $[G:G_a] = n$. Since G_a is transitive of degree $n-1$ we have $(n-1) \mid |G_a|$. Hence $n(n-1) \mid |G|$. Of course $2 \mid n(n-1)$ so G has even order. This yields the following

COROLLARY 7.4. Let G be a permutation group of prime degree and odd order. Then G is solvable.

8. FROBENIUS GROUPS

Let $F = GF(p)$. The function $cx+d \neq x$ with $c, d \in F$, $c \neq 0$ cannot fix two elements of F. Hence the group $G = \{cx+d\}$ has the property that $G_{a,b} = (G_a)_b = \langle 1 \rangle$. Now let

G be any transitive group on set A. We say G is 3/2-transitive if $G_a \neq \langle 1 \rangle$ is 1/2-transitive on $A-\{a\}$. If in fact $G_a \neq \langle 1 \rangle$ and G_a is semiregular then G is called a Frobenius group. Thus G is a Frobenius group if and only if $G_a \neq \langle 1 \rangle$ but $G_{a,b} = \langle 1 \rangle$ for all $a \neq b$.

Clearly a Frobenius group is 3/2-transitive. A partial converse is given by the following

THEOREM 8.1. If G is a 3/2-transitive permutation group then either G is primitive or G is a Frobenius group.

Proof. If C is a subset of A, the set of points being permuted, we let G_C denote the subgroup of G fixing all points of C and we let $G_{\langle C \rangle}$ denote the subgroup of G fixing C setwise.

Let G be 3/2-transitive of degree n and assume G is imprimitive. Say $A = B_1 \cup B_2 \cup \ldots \cup B_r$ is a system of imprimitivity, that is the set of all conjugates of a fixed nontrivial subset of imprimitivity. Set $|B_i| = k$ with $1 < k < n$. Let all the orbits of G_a on $A-\{a\}$ have size m.

If $a \in B_i$, then $B_i G_a = B_i$ and B_i is a union of $\{a\}$ and orbits of G_a in $A - \{a\}$. Hence $k = |B_i| \equiv 1 \mod m$ and so $(k, m) = 1$. If $a \notin B_i$ then $B_i G_a$ is a union of orbits of G_a in $A - \{a\}$ and hence $m \mid |B_i G_a|$. Also $B_i G_a$ is a union of some B_j so $k \mid |B_i G_a|$. Hence $mk \mid |B_i G_a|$. Since clearly $|B_i G_a| \leq |B_i| m = km$ we have $|B_i G_a| = km$ and $B_i G_a$ is the union of precisely m B_j's. Thus $[G_a : G_{a, \langle B_i \rangle}] = m$.

Now let $a_i \in B_i$, $a_j \in B_j$, $i \neq j$. We have by the above $[G_{a_j} : G_{a_j, \langle B_i \rangle}] = m$. Also $[G_{a_j} : G_{a_j, a_i}] = m$ and $G_{a_j, a_i} \subseteq G_{a_j, \langle B_i \rangle}$. Hence $G_{a_j, a_i} = G_{a_j, \langle B_i \rangle}$. Since this is true for all $a_i \in B_i$ we have $G_{a_j, a_i} = G_{a_j, B_i} \subseteq G_{B_i} \subseteq G_{\bar{a}_i, a_i}$ where $\bar{a}_i \in B_i$, $\bar{a}_i \neq a_i$. Since $|G_{a_j, a_i}| = |G_{\bar{a}_i, a_i}|$ we have $G_{a_j, a_i} = G_{B_i}$. By symmetry $G_{B_j} = G_{a_j, a_i} = G_{a_i, a_j} = G_{B_i}$.

Fix i and let j run over all possible subscripts. Then the above shows that $G_{B_i} = G_A = \langle 1 \rangle$ and so $G_{a_i, a_j} = \langle 1 \rangle$. Since G is 3/2-transitive it follows that for all $a \neq b$, $|G_{a,b}| = |G_{a_i, a_j}| = 1$ and thus G is a Frobenius group.

Let G be a group and D a subset of G. Then D is called a T.I. set (trivial intersection set) if $g \in G$ implies that either $D^g = D$ or $D^g \cap D \subseteq \{1\}$. We can describe a Frobenius group abstractly as follows.

PROPOSITION 8.2. A group G has a faithful permutation representation in which it is a Frobenius group if and only if G has a proper subgroup H which is a T.I. set with $\mathcal{N}(H) = H$.

Proof. Suppose G is a Frobenius group and set $H = G_a$. By assumption $\langle 1 \rangle < H < G$. If $g \in G-H$, then $H^g = G_a{}^g = G_{ag} = G_b$ where $b = ag \neq a$. Thus $H^g \cap H = G_a \cap G_b = G_{a,b} = \langle 1 \rangle$. Hence H is a T.I. set and $\mathcal{N}(H) = H$.

Conversely given group G with subgroup H then G permutes transitively the right cosets of H by right multiplication. Thus if $\{x_1, \ldots, x_n\}$ is a set of coset representatives of H, then we have a homomorphism of G into $\mathrm{Sym}\,\{Hx_i\}$ given by $g \to \begin{pmatrix} Hx_i \\ Hx_i g \end{pmatrix}$. Let $a = Hx_i$, $b = Hx_j$ with $i \neq j$. Then clearly $G_a = H^{x_i}$, $G_b = H^{x_j}$ and $G_{a,b} = H^{x_i} \cap H^{x_j}$. Now $x_j x_i^{-1} \notin H = \mathcal{N}(H)$ and hence $H^{x_i} \neq H^{x_j}$. Hence since H is a T.I. set, $G_{a,b} = \langle 1 \rangle$. This shows that the representation is faithful and G is a Frobenius group.

We will show later that G can be represented as a Frobenius group in essentially one way.

Now suppose G is a Frobenius group of degree n. If $|G_a| = m$ then $|G| = nm$ and since G_a is semiregular on the set $A - \{a\}$ we have $m | (n-1)$. Since G_a is a T.I. set we have $|\bigcup_{a \in A} G_a^{\#}| = n(m-1)$ and hence there are n remaining elements in G. These elements are those g with $\theta(g) = 0$ and $g = 1$. If these elements form a subgroup N, then N is clearly a regular normal subgroup of G. We will show later that N always exists. This subgroup is called the Frobenius kernel. The subgroups G_a are the Frobenius complements. In the remainder of the section we will show the existence of N under certain special circumstances.

PROPOSITION 8.3. Let G be a Frobenius group with $|G_a|$ even. Then G has an abelian regular normal subgroup.

Proof. Let G have degree n so that $G \subseteq \mathrm{Sym}(n)$. Suppose that G_a has r elements of order 2. Now each such element fixes only one point and is therefore a product of $(n-1)/2$ distinct transpositions. Since G_a is a T.I. set, G has precisely rn elements of order 2 and thus $r \cdot n(n-1)/2$ transpositions occur. Note that since n is odd an element of G of order 2 must belong to some G_a. Now $\mathrm{Sym}(n)$ contains precisely $n(n-1)/2$ transpositions. Thus if $r > 1$ then G has two distinct elements of order 2 having a common transposition among their cycles. Say $x = (1\ 2)x'$, $y = (1\ 2)y'$ with $x \neq y$, $x, y \in G$. Also x', y' do not move points 1 and 2. Then $xy^{-1} \neq 1$ fixes two points, a contradiction. Thus $r = 1$.

Let T be the set of elements of G of order 2 so that $|T| = n$. Let N be the set of elements of G with $g = 1$ or $\Theta(g) = 0$ so that $|N| = n$. We show that if $x, y \in T$ then $xy \in N$. If not then say xy fixes point a and let $ax = b$. Then $by = a$ and since x and y have order 2, $ay = b$ and $bx = a$. Thus $bxy = b$. If $a \neq b$ then $xy \in G_{a,b} = \langle 1 \rangle$ and hence $xy = 1 \in N$. On the other hand if $a = b$ then $x, y \in G_a$ and hence $x = y$ and $xy = 1 \in N$.

Now if $x \in T$ then $xT \subseteq N$ and $|xT| = n = |N|$. Thus $xT = N$ and similarly $Tx = N$. Also $TT = N$. Finally since x has order 2, $NN = (Tx)(xT) = TT = N$ and so N is a subgroup. This implies that N is a regular normal subgroup of G. Now $xT = N$ so if $g \in G$ then $g = xy$ for some $y \in T$. This yields $g^x = x^{-1}(xy)x = yx = (xy)^{-1} = g^{-1}$. If $g, h \in N$ then $g^{-1}h^{-1} = g^x h^x = (gh)^x = (gh)^{-1} = h^{-1}g^{-1}$ and so g and h commute. Thus N is abelian and the result follows.

PROPOSITION 8.4. Let G be a Frobenius group of degree n and of maximal possible order, namely $n(n-1)$. Then $n = p^k$ for some prime p and G has a regular normal elementary abelian subgroup.

Proof. Again let $N = \{g \mid \Theta(g) = 0 \text{ or } g = 1\}$ so that $|N| = n$. Let prime p divide n and let $x \in G$ have order p. If $x \in G_a$ then p divides $|G_a| = n-1$, a contradiction. Thus $G_a{}^x \cap G_a = \langle 1 \rangle$ and hence $\mathcal{L}(x) \cap G_a = \langle 1 \rangle$. Then $|\mathcal{L}(x)G_a| = |\mathcal{L}(x)|(n-1) \leq n(n-1)$ and thus if $\mathrm{Cl}\, x$ denotes the conjugacy class of x then $|\mathrm{Cl}\ x| = [G:\mathcal{C}(x)] \geq n-1$. Now no element of $\mathrm{Cl}\ x$ can belong to any G_a and hence $\mathrm{Cl}\ x \subseteq N-\{1\}$. This yields $N-\{1\} = \mathrm{Cl}\ x$ and so p is the unique prime divisor of n.

Now G has a Sylow p-subgroup of order n since $(n, n-1) = 1$ and thus N is a group and hence a regular normal subgroup of G. Since $N^{\#} = \mathrm{Cl}\ x$ we see that G permutes the elements of $N^{\#}$ transitively by conjugation. Hence N is an elementary abelian p-group and the result follows.

In the next chapter we will develop sufficient machinery to study closely the structure of Frobenius groups.

CHAPTER II

MACHINERY

9. NILPOTENT GROUPS

We first compute the automorphism group of a cyclic group of prime power order. We let J denote the ring of rational integers and J_n the integers modulo n. Also $G(n)$ will denote the cyclic group of order n.

THEOREM 9.1. Let p be a prime. If $p > 2$ and $t > 0$ then $\mathrm{Aut}\ G(p^t) \simeq G((p-1)p^{t-1})$. If $p = 2$ and $t > 1$ then $\mathrm{Aut}\ G(2^t) \simeq G(2) \times G(2^{t-2})$.

Proof. Say $p^t = n$ and let $G(p^t) = \langle x \rangle$. If σ is an automorphism of $\langle x \rangle$ then $x\sigma = x^r$ for some r and σ is uniquely determined by r modulo n. Let σ_r be defined by $x^i\sigma_r = x^{ir}$. Then $x^i(\sigma_r\sigma_s) = x^{irs} = x^i\sigma_{rs}$. Thus σ_r is an automorphism if and only if r is a unit modulo n. With this we see easily that $\mathrm{Aut}\, G(n) \simeq J_n^*$, the group of units in J_n. If $n = p^t$ then clearly $|J_n^*| = p^t - p^{t-1} = p^{t-1}(p-1)$.

We show first that J_n^* has an element of order $p-1$. There is an obvious map $J_n \to J_p$ and this induces a map $J_n^* \to J_p^*$. Now J_p is a field so as is well known J_p^* is cyclic of order $p-1$. Then J_n^* has an element whose order is divisible by $(p-1)$ and a suitable power of this element yields one of order $p-1$.

Let $c = 1 + kp^m$ with $m \geq 1$. Then since $3m \geq m+2$ $c^p \equiv 1 + kp^{m+1} + k^2p^{2m}\, p(p+1)/2 \mod p^{m+2}$. This shows that if $c \equiv 1 \mod p^m$ then $c^p \equiv 1 \mod p^{m+1}$. Moreover with the exception of $p = 2$, $m = 1$ if $c \equiv 1 \mod p^m$ but $c \not\equiv 1 \mod p^{m+1}$ then $c^p \not\equiv 1 \mod p^{m+2}$.

If $p > 2$ then the above show that $c = 1+p$ has order p^{t-1} in J_n^*. Since $|J_n^*| = p^{t-1}(p-1)$ and J_n^* is abelian, this implies that it is cyclic.

Now let $p = 2$. Then $c = 1+4 = 5$ has order 2^{t-2} in

J_n^*. But $-1 \notin \langle c \rangle$ since every element of $\langle c \rangle$ is $\equiv 1 \mod 4$. Since -1 has order 2 we see that $J_n^* = \langle -1 \rangle \times \langle 5 \rangle$ and the result follows.

The above methods also yield the following information.

PROPOSITION 9.2. Let $G(p^t) = \langle x \rangle$. If $p > 2$, $t > 1$ then the unique subgroup of Aut $G(p^t)$ of order p is generated by the element $x \to x^{1+p^{t-1}}$. If $p = 2$, $t > 2$ then the three elements of order 2 in Aut $G(p^t)$ are $x \to x^{-1}$, $x \to x^{-1+2^{t-1}}$, $x \to x^{1+2^{t-1}}$. Moreover only the last of these has a square root in Aut $G(p^t)$.

PROPOSITION 9.3. Let $G(p)$ and $G(p^{t-1})$ denote the obvious characteristic subgroups of $G(p^t)$. Let σ be an automorphism of $G(p^t)$ of order prime to p. If σ centralizes $G(p^t)/G(p^{t-1})$ or $G(p)$ then $\sigma = 1$.

Proof. Say $\sigma : x \to x^r$ where $G(p^t) = \langle x \rangle$. If σ centralizes $G(p^t)/G(p^{t-1})$ then $r = 1+kp$. If σ centralizes $G(p)$ then $p^{t-1}(1-r) \equiv 0 \mod p^t$ and hence also $r = 1+kp$.

Now we can assume that $p \neq 2$ since Aut $G(2^t)$ is a 2-group. Hence $r = 1+kp$ has order a power of p in $J_{p^t}^*$. This yields $\sigma = 1$.

THEOREM 9.4. Let G be a p-group of order p^{n+1} and suppose G has a cyclic subgroup of index p. Then either G is cyclic or G is generated by elements x and y satisfying $x^{p^n} = 1$ and one of the following.

i. $y^p = 1$, $y^{-1}xy = x$ (abelian group)

ii. $p > 2$ or $p = 2$, $n \geq 3$: $y^p = 1$, $y^{-1}xy = x^{1+p^{n-1}}$ (ordinary nonabelian group)

iii. $p = 2$: $y^2 = 1$, $y^{-1}xy = x^{-1}$ (dihedral group)

iv. $p = 2$: $y^2 = 1$, $y^{-1}xy = x^{-1+2^{n-1}}$ (semidihedral group)

v. $p = 2$: $y^2 = x^{2^{n-1}}$, $y^{-1}xy = x^{-1}$ (quaternion group).

Moreover groups (i) and (ii) have characteristic abelian subgroups of type (p, p).

<u>Proof</u>. Let $A = \langle x \rangle$ be the given cyclic subgroup

of G. Since $[G:A] = p$, $A \triangle G$. If A is central in G then G is abelian and hence G is cyclic or type (i). We suppose that A is not central so $\mathcal{L}(A) = A$ since A is a maximal subgroup.

Let $G = \langle x, w \rangle$. Since $\langle x \rangle \triangle G$, w acts on $\langle x \rangle$ by conjugation. It acts nontrivially since $\mathcal{L}(A) = A$ and has order p in this action since $w^p \in \mathcal{L}(A)$. Let $w^p = x^r$. Clearly $w^{-1}x^r w = x^r$. By Proposition 9.2 we know the possible actions of w on $\langle x \rangle$.

Suppose first that $w^{-1}xw = x^w = x^{1+p^{n-1}}$. This applies for $p > 2$ or $p = 2$, $n \geq 3$. Since $w^{-1}x^r w = x^r$ we see that $r = ps$. Now

$$(x^{-s}w)^p = x^{-s}wx^{-s}w \ldots x^{-s}w$$
$$= w^p (x^{-s})^{w^p} (x^{-s})^{w^{p-1}} \ldots (x^{-s})^w.$$

Since $(x^{-s})^{w^i} = x^{-s(1+p^{n-1})^i} = x^{-s(1+ip^{n-1})}$ we have

$$(x^{-s}w)^p = w^p\, x^{-s\sum_i (1+ip^{n-1})} = w^p\, x^{-s\{p+p^n(p+1)/2\}}.$$

Now $w^p = x^{sp}$ so $(x^{-s}w)^p = x^{-sp^n(p+1)/2}$. If $p > 2$ then set $y = x^{-s}w$. We see that $y^{-1}xy = x^{1+p^{n-1}}$ and from the above since $p^n \mid -sp^n(p+1)/2$ we have $y^p = 1$. Hence G is type (ii) here. If $p = 2$ set $y = x^{-s(1+2^{n-2})}w$. Then again $y^{-1}xy = x^{1+2^{n-1}}$. Also

$$y^2 = x^{-s(1+2^{n-2})}w^2\{w^{-1}x^{-s(1+2^{n-2})}w\} = x^{-s2^{2n-3}}.$$

Since $n \geq 3$, $2n-3 \geq n$ and $y^2 = 1$. Thus again G is type (ii).

The remaining possibilities hold only for $p=2$. Suppose first that $w^{-1}xw = x^{-1}$ and set $y = w$. Then $y^{-1}xy = x^{-1}$ and since $y^{-1}y^2y^{-1} = y^2$ we see that $y^2 = 1$ or $x^{2^{n-1}}$. These are groups (iii) and (v). Now let $w^{-1}xw = x^{-1+2^{n-1}}$ so we must have $n \geq 3$. Since $w^{-1}w^2w = w^2$ we have $w^2 = 1$ or $x^{2^{n-1}}$. If $w^2 = 1$ set $y = w$. If $w^2 = x^{2^{n-1}}$ then set $y = xw$. Here $y^2 = (xw)^2 = xw^2\{w^{-1}xw\} = 1$ and thus in both cases G is type (iv).

This completes the first part of the proof. It remains to show that groups (i) and (ii) have characteristic abelian subgroups of type (p, p). Set $B = \langle x^{p^{n-1}}, y\rangle$. Since both $x^{p^{n-1}}$ and y commute and have order p we see that B is abelian of type (p, p). We will show that every element of G of order p is contained in B. This will show that B is characteristic. If G is type (i) the result is obvious so we assume G is type (ii).

Let $g \in G$ have order p. Now clearly $G' = \langle x^{p^{n-1}} \rangle$ and so $\bar{g}$ the image of g in G/G' has order 1 or p in G/G'. This latter group is abelian and is generated by $\bar{x}$ and $\bar{y}$. This clearly implies that $\bar{g} \in \langle \bar{x}^{p^{n-2}}, \bar{y} \rangle$ and hence $g \in \langle x^{p^{n-2}}, y \rangle$. If $n \geq 3$ then $\langle x^{p^{n-2}}, y \rangle$ is an abelian group and thus clearly $g \in \langle x^{p^{n-1}}, y \rangle = B$. We need only consider $n = 2$ now and by assumption only for $p > 2$. If $g = x^i y^j$ then we see easily that

$$1 = g^p = x^i y^j x^i y^j \ldots x^i y^j = (x^i)^{y^{pj}} (x^i)^{y^{(p-1)j}} \ldots (x^i)^{y^j}$$
$$= x^{i \Sigma_k (1 + kjp)} = x^{i\{p + jp^2(p+1)/2\}} = x^{ip}$$

since $p > 2$. This yields $p \mid i$ and $g \in B$. This completes the proof of the theorem.

The following few results are almost immediate consequences of the above.

PROPOSITION 9.5. Let G be a p-group and suppose that G is not cyclic, dihedral, semidihedral or quaternion. Then G has a normal abelian subgroup of type (p, p).

Proof. Let A be a subgroup of G maximal with respect to being normal and cyclic. Since $|G| \geq p$, $|A| \geq p$. By assumption $A \neq G$. Suppose first that $\mathcal{C}(A) > A$. Since $\mathcal{C}(A) \triangle G$ we can choose $B \triangle G$ with $A < B \subseteq \mathcal{C}(A)$ and $[B:A] = p$. Clearly B is abelian and by the maximality of A, B is not cyclic. Hence B is a type (i) group of the preceeding theorem and B has a characteristic abelian subgroup D of type (p, p). Since $B \triangle G$ we have $D \triangle G$ and the result follows here.

Thus we can assume that $\mathcal{C}(A) = A$. Now G acts on A by conjugation and the kernel is clearly $\mathcal{C}(A)$. Thus G/A is isomorphic to a subgroup of Aut A and hence is abelian. In particular if $B \supseteq A$ then $B \triangle G$. Let $B > A$ with $[B:A] = p$. Then B is type (ii), (iii), (iv) or (v) of the preceeding theorem. If B is type (ii), then B has a characteristic abelian subgroup D of type (p, p) and hence $D \triangle G$. We can assume then that for all such B, B is type (iii), (iv) or (v). In particular we must have $p = 2$ and G/A is a subgroup of Aut A which does not contain the automorphism $x \rightarrow x^{1+2^{n-1}}$ where $A = \langle x \rangle$ and $|A| = 2^n$. From the nature of Aut A this yields $|G/A| = 2$

and hence $G = B$ is type (iii), (iv) or (v).

COROLLARY 9.6. Let G be a p-group with $\mathfrak{Z}_2(G)$, the second center of G, cyclic. Then G is either cyclic, dihedral, semidihedral or quaternion.

Proof. If G is not one of the above exceptions, then G has a normal abelian subgroup D of type (p, p). Since $(G, D) < D$, $(G, (G, D)) < (G, D)$ and $|D| = p^2$ we have $(G, (G, D)) = \langle 1 \rangle$. Hence $D \subseteq \mathfrak{Z}_2(G)$ and $\mathfrak{Z}_2(G)$ is not cyclic.

COROLLARY 9.7. (Roquette) Let G be a p-group and suppose that every normal abelian subgroup of G is cyclic. Then G is cyclic, dihedral, semidihedral or quaternion.

COROLLARY 9.8. Let G be a p-group with precisely one subgroup of order p. Then G is either cyclic or quaternion.

Proof. Certainly G cannot have a subgroup of type

(p, p). Hence by Proposition 9.5 G is one of four possibilities. From the nature of the generators and relations for these groups we see that G must be cyclic or quaternion. Clearly a cyclic p-group has a unique subgroup of order p. Now let $G = gp\langle x, y \mid x^{2^n} = 1,\ y^2 = x^{2^{n-1}},\ y^{-1}xy = x^{-1}\rangle$, and let $w \in G$ have order 2. If $w \in \langle x \rangle$ then certainly $w = x^{2^{n-1}}$. If $w \notin \langle x \rangle$ then $w = x^i y$ for some i. Hence $1 = w^2 = x^i y x^i y = x^i y^2 \{y^{-1} x^i y\} = x^i y^2 x^{-i} = y^2 = x^{2^{n-1}}$, a contradiction. Thus G has a unique element of order 2.

These quaternion groups will play an important role in some later work. We list now properties of these groups which are relevent for this work.

PROPOSITION 9.9. Let G be the quaternion group of order 8. Then

i. Every proper subgroup of G is cyclic.

ii. Aut $G \simeq$ Sym(4), a group of order 24.

iii. If $\sigma \in$ Aut G has order 3, then σ transitively permutes the three noncentral classes of G.

Proof. Let $H < G$ so that $|H| \leq 4$. Since G has a unique element of order 2 and H is abelian, H is cyclic and (i) follows.

Now G has three distinct subgroups of order 4 say $\langle u\rangle, \langle v\rangle, \langle w\rangle$. If z is the unique element of G of order 2, then $u^2 = v^2 = w^2 = z$, $(u,v) = (u,w) = (v,w) = z$ and $\langle u,v\rangle = \langle u,w\rangle = \langle v,w\rangle = G$. Thus we see that $\mathrm{Sym}\{u,v,w\}$ is contained in Aut G in the obvious manner. Also $\mathrm{Sym}\{u,v,w\} \cap \mathrm{Inn}\, G = \langle 1\rangle$ since $\langle u\rangle, \langle v\rangle, \langle w\rangle$ are normal in G. Thus since $\mathrm{Inn}\, G \triangle \mathrm{Aut}\, G$ and $|\mathrm{Inn}\, G| = 4$ we see that $\mathrm{Aut}\, G \supseteq (\mathrm{Inn}\, G)(\mathrm{Sym}\{u,v,w\})$ and the latter group is easily seen to be isomorphic to Sym(4). If $\sigma \in \mathrm{Aut}\, G$ then there are at most six possibilities for $u\sigma$. Once $u\sigma$ is known there are at most four possibilities for $v\sigma$. Hence since $\langle u,v\rangle = G$ there are at most 24 possibilities for σ. Thus $\mathrm{Aut}\, G \cong \mathrm{Sym}(4)$.

Now let $\sigma \in \mathrm{Aut}\, G$ have order 3. Then σ permutes the three subgroups $\langle u\rangle, \langle v\rangle, \langle w\rangle$. If σ fixes one such subgroup it fixes all and hence $u\sigma = u$ or u^{-1}, $v\sigma = v$ or v^{-1}, $w\sigma = w$ or w^{-1} so $\sigma^2 = 1$, a contradiction. Hence σ permutes these transitively. Since the noncentral classes of G are $\{u, u^{-1}\}$, $\{v, v^{-1}\}$, $\{w, w^{-1}\}$ the result follows.

PROPOSITION 9.10. Let G be a quaternion group of order ≥ 16. Then

i. Every subgroup of G is cyclic or quaternion.

ii. If N is a nonabelian normal subgroup of G, then $[G:N] = 1$ or 2.

iii. G has a characteristic cyclic subgroup A of index 2.

iv. Aut G is a 2-group.

v. G has three conjugacy classes of elements of order 4. One of these consists of the two elements of A of order 4. The other two each consist of half the elements of $G-A$.

Proof. Since G has a unique element of order 2 so does every subgroup. Hence by Corollary 9.8 the subgroups of G are cyclic or quaternion. Write $G = \langle x, y \mid x^{2^n} = 1,\ y^2 = x^{2^{n-1}},\ y^{-1}xy = x^{-1} \rangle$ and let $A = \langle x \rangle$. We have shown in the proof of Proposition 9.8 that every element of G-A has order 4. Thus the generators of A are the only elements of G of order $2^n > 4$ and so A is characteristic in G. This yields (i) and (iii).

Let N be a normal nonabelian subgroup of G. Then $N \nsubseteq A$ so let $w \in N-A$. Clearly $w^2 = x^{2^{n-1}}$ and $w^{-1}xw = x^{-1}$. Since $N \triangle G$, N contains the element $(w,x) = (w^{-1}x^{-1}w)x = x^2$ and hence $N \supseteq \langle x^2, w\rangle$ a subgroup of G of index 2. Thus (ii) follows.

Suppose by way of contradiction that Aut G is not a 2-group. Let $\sigma \in \text{Aut } G$ be an element of order $p > 2$. Since A is characteristic in G, $\sigma | A$ is an automorphism of A. But Aut A is a 2-group so σ fixes every element of A. Now $\langle\sigma\rangle$ permutes the 2^n elements in G-A and hence there exists $w \in G-A$ with $w\sigma = w$. Since $G = \langle A, w\rangle$, σ fixes all of G, a contradiction and (iv) follows.

Clearly $\{x^{2^{n-2}}, x^{-2^{n-2}}\}$, the set of elements of A of order 4, is a class of G. Let $w \in G-A$. Since $w^{-1}xw = x^{-1}$ we see that $\mathcal{L}(w) = \langle x^{2^{n-1}}, w\rangle = \langle w\rangle$ and thus $|\text{Cl } w| = |G|/4 = |G-A|/2$. Finally since clearly $\text{Cl } w \subseteq G-A$ the result follows.

10. GROUP EXTENSIONS

Let A and B be groups with A abelian. Suppose we have a fixed homomorphism of B into Aut A. In this way we let B act on A and we use the notation a^b for the image of $a \in A$ under the action of $b \in B$.

A factor system is a map from $B \times B$ to A satisfying the axiom below. Here we let (b, c) denote the image in A of $[b, c] \in B \times B$. Note that this differs from our usual notation in which (,) denotes a commutator. We will use this special notation only in this section. The axiom is

$$(*) \quad \text{If } b, c, d \in B \text{ then } (bc, d)(b, c)^d = (b, cd)(c, d).$$

If $(,)_1$ and $(,)_2$ are two factor systems then since A is abelian we see that the pointwise product of these two functions $(,)_1(,)_2$ is also a factor system. Hence the set of these factor systems forms a group F(A, B). Clearly F(A, B) is a subgroup of the direct product of $|B|^2$ copies of A. Thus F(A, B) is abelian and $|F(A, B)| \mid |A|^{|B|^2}$. We repeat again that F(A, B) depends strongly on the fixed homomorphism of B into Aut A and for different homomorphisms we get different F(A, B)'s.

If $(\, , \,)_1$ and $(\, , \,)_2$ are two factor systems we say that these are equivalent if there exists a function $\alpha : B \to A$ with

$$(**) \qquad (b,c)_1 = (b,c)_2 \, \alpha(bc)^{-1} \alpha(b)^c \alpha(c).$$

It is easy to see that this is indeed an equivalence relation which is compatible with the group multiplication in F(A, B). Thus the set of factor systems equivalent to the identity (that is, the function $(b,c) = 1$ for all b, c) forms a normal subgroup of F(A, B). We denote by H(A, B) the quotient group. The elements of H(A, B) are then the equivalence classes. We have of course $|H(A,B)| \mid |A|^{|B|^2}$.

Before we continue our study of the group H(A, B) we first see in what context they occur. Let us note the following. Suppose $A \triangleleft G$ and A is abelian. Then G acts on A by conjugation. Since A is abelian, the kernel of the action contains A. Hence we can speak of G/A acting on A.

THEOREM 10.1. (Schreier) Let G be a group with a normal abelian subgroup A. Let $G/A = B$ and let the action of B on A be given. For each $b \in B$, let $\bar{b} \in G$ be a coset representative for b. If $b, c \in B$, let $(b,c) \in A$ be defined by $\bar{b}\,\bar{c} = \overline{bc}\,(b,c)$. Then with respect to the action of B on A the function $(\ ,\ )$ is a factor system. Moreove if we choose another set of coset representatives then the new and the old factor systems are equivalent.

Conversely given B and abelian A with a given action of B on A. Let the function $(\ ,\ )$ be a factor system. Let $G = \{[b,a] \mid a \in A,\ b \in B\}$ and define multiplication by $[b_1, a_1][b_2, a_2] = [b_1 b_2, (b_1, b_2) a_1^{b_2} a_2]$. Then G is a group, $A \simeq \bar{A} = \{[1,a]\} \Delta G$ and $G/\bar{A} \simeq B$.

Proof. First let $(b,c) \in A$ be defined by $\bar{b}\,\bar{c} = \overline{bc}\,(b,c)$. If $b, c, d \in B$ then

$$\bar{b}\,(\bar{c}\,\bar{d}) = \bar{b}\,(\overline{cd}\,(c,d)) = \overline{bcd}\,(b,cd)(c,d)$$

$$(\bar{b}\,\bar{c})\,\bar{d} = \overline{bc}\,(b,c)\,\bar{d} = \overline{bc}\,\bar{d}\,(b,c)^d = \overline{bcd}\,(bc,d)\,(b,c)^d .$$

Hence $(b,cd)(c,d) = (bc,d)(b,c)^d$ and the function $(\ ,\ )$ is a factor system.

If for $b \in B$, $b^* \in G$ is another coset representative, then $b^* = \bar{b}\alpha(b)$ where $\alpha(b) \in A$. Let $(\; , \;)_*$ denote this new factor system. Then

$$(bc)^* (b,c)_* = b^* c^* = \bar{b}\alpha(b)\, \bar{c}\alpha(c) = \bar{b}\, \bar{c}\, \alpha(b)^c\alpha(c)$$
$$= \overline{bc}\, (b,c)\alpha(b)^c\alpha(c) = (bc)^*\alpha(bc)^{-1}\, (b,c)\alpha(b)^c\alpha(c)$$

and hence $(b,c)_* = (b,c)\alpha(bc)^{-1}\alpha(b)^c\alpha(c)$. Thus $(\; , \;)_*$ and $(\; , \;)$ are equivalent.

We consider the converse. Clearly G is closed under multiplication. We show it is associative. Now

$$([b_1, a_1][b_2, a_2])\, [b_3, a_3] = [b_1b_2, (b_1, b_2)a_1^{\,b_2}a_2][b_3, a_3]$$
$$= [b_1b_2b_3, (b_1b_2, b_3)(b_1, b_2)^{b_3}a_1^{\,b_2b_3}a_2^{\,b_3}a_3]$$

and

$$[b_1, a_1]\, ([b_2, a_2]\, [b_3, a_3]) = [b_1, a_1][b_2b_3, (b_2, b_3)a_2^{\,b_3}a_3]$$
$$= [b_1b_2b_3, (b_1, b_2b_3)a_1^{\,b_2b_3}(b_2, b_3)a_2^{\,b_3}a_3].$$

Thus associativity follows from (*).

We show now that G is left cancellative. Say $[b, a][b_1, a_1] = [b, a][b_2, a_2]$. Then $bb_1 = bb_2$ and also $(b, b_1)a^{b_1}a_1 = (b, b_2)a^{b_2}a_2$. This clearly yields $b_1 = b_2$ and then $a_1 = a_2$. Hence since G is finite, it is a group.

The map $[b, a] \to b$ is clearly a homomorphism of G onto B with kernel $\bar{A} = \{[1, a]\}$. It remains to show that $A \simeq \bar{A}$. Define a map $A \to \bar{A}$ by $a \to [1, a(1, 1)^{-1}]$. Since it is easy to see that this is an isomorphism, the result follows.

Thus in some sense H(A, B) denotes the group of extensions of A by B. If a factor system is equivalent to the identity function then G contains an isomorphic copy $\bar{B}$ of B with $\bar{B} \cap A = \langle 1 \rangle$ and $G = A\bar{B}$. In this case we say that the extension is split.

THEOREM 10.2. The period of H(A, B) divides $|A|$ and $|B|$.

Proof. We have F(A, B) contained in the direct product of $|B|^2$ copies of A. Hence the period of F(A, B) divides $|A|$ and of course the same must hold for H(A, B).

Let (,) be a factor system and let $|B| = n$. Set $\alpha(c) = \prod_{b \in B} (b, c)$. Multiplying (*) over all $b \in B$ yields $\alpha(d)\alpha(c)^d = \alpha(cd)(c, d)^n$. Hence the factor system $(\, , \,)^n$

is equivalent to 1 and thus the period of $H(A, B)$ divides $n = |B|$.

COROLLARY 10.3. If A is abelian and $|A|$ and $|B|$ are relatively prime, then every extension of A by B is split.

The following result eliminates the assumption in the above that A is abelian. If G is a group, then a Hall subgroup H is a subgroup whose order $|H|$ and index $[G:H]$ are relatively prime.

THEOREM 10.4. (Schur-Zassenhaus) Let H be a normal Hall subgroup of G. Then there exists a subgroup B of G with $B \cap H = \langle 1 \rangle$ and $HB = G$.

Proof. By induction on $|G|$. Suppose there exists $N \triangle G$ with $\langle 1 \rangle < N < H$. Then H/N is a normal Hall subgroup of G/N and hence this group has a subgroup L/N with $HL = G$ and $L \cap H = N$. Certainly $L < G$ and N is a normal Hall subgroup of L. Now by induction again we can find $B \subseteq L$ with $B \cap N = \langle 1 \rangle$ and $NB = L$. Then $H \cap B = H \cap L \cap B = N \cap B = \langle 1 \rangle$ and $HB = HNB = HL = G$. Thus the result follows here. Hence we can assume that no such N exists.

We can clearly assume that $H \neq \langle 1 \rangle$. Let $P \neq \langle 1 \rangle$ be a Sylow p-subgroup of H and hence one of G. Then H contains all Sylow p-subgroups of G. Now G permutes all these by conjugation and by Sylow's theorem H is transitive. Thus Proposition 4.8 yields $G = H\mathfrak{N}(P)$. Suppose $\mathfrak{N}(P) < G$. Then $H \cap \mathfrak{N}(P) = K$ is a normal Hall subgroup of $\mathfrak{N}(P)$ and by induction we can find $B \subseteq \mathfrak{N}(P)$ with $K \cap B = \langle 1 \rangle$ and $KB = \mathfrak{N}(P)$. Since $H \cap B = H \cap \mathfrak{N}(P) \cap B = K \cap B = \langle 1 \rangle$ and $HB = HKB = H\mathfrak{N}(P) = G$ the result follows.

Thus we can assume that $\mathfrak{N}(P) = G$ and so $P \triangle G$. This yields the facts that $H = P$ and also that P has no proper characteristic subgroup. Thus P is abelian and the result follows from Corollary 10.3.

The subgroup B above is called a complement for H. If B is such a complement then so is any conjugate of B. The question we consider now is whether these are the only complements for H.

THEOREM 10.5. (Zassenhaus) Let H be a normal Hall subgroup of G. If either H or G/H is solvable then any two complements of H in G are conjugate.

<u>Proof</u>. Suppose first that H is abelian. Let B and E be two complements for H. If $e \in E$ then there exists a unique $b \in B$ with $e = b\alpha(b)$ and $\alpha(b) \in H$. If also $f \in E$ and $f = c\alpha(c)$ then

$$bc\ \alpha(bc) = ef = b\ \alpha(b)\ c\ \alpha(c) = bc\ \alpha(b)^c\ \alpha(c)$$

so we have $\alpha(bc) = \alpha(b)^c \alpha(c)$. Let $|B| = n$ and set $d = \prod_{b \in B} \alpha(b)$. Multiplying the preceeding equation over all $b \in B$ yields $d = d^c\ \alpha(c)^n$. Since n is prime to $|H|$, H has unique n^{th} roots. If $a \in H$ with $a^n = d$ then we have $a = a^c\ \alpha(c)$. This yields

$$c^a = a^{-1}ca = c(c^{-1}a^{-1}c)a = c(a^c)^{-1}a = c\ \alpha(c) = f$$

and hence $B^a = E$. Thus the result follows in this case.

Now let H be solvable and let B and E be two complements. We show that B and E are conjugate by induction on $|G|$. Suppose H has a subgroup N with

$\langle 1 \rangle < N < H$ and $N \triangle G$. Then by induction BN/N and EN/N are conjugate in G/N. Choose $g \in G$ with $E^g \subseteq BN$. Then E^g and B are complements of normal solvable Hall subgroup N in $BN < G$. By induction there exists $h \in BN$ with $E^{gh} = B$ and the result follows here. On the other hand if no such N exists then H has no proper characteristic subgroup. Since H is solvable, it is abelian and the result follows from the work of the preceeding paragraph.

Now let G/H be solvable and let B and E be complements for H. We show that B and E are conjugate by induction on $|G|$. Let U be a minimal normal subgroup of B. Since B is solvable U is a p-group for some prime p. Set $V = E \cap HU$ so that $V \triangle E$ and $V \cong U$. Clearly U and V are Sylow p-subgroups of HU and hence there exists $g \in HU$ with $V^g = U$. Thus $U \triangle B$ and $U \triangle E^g$ and both B and E^g are complements of $H \cap N$ in N where $N = \mathcal{N}(U)$. Since B/U and E^g/U are complements of $(H \cap N)U/U$ in N/U and $|N/U| < |G|$ induction implies that B/U and E^g/U are conjugate in N/U. Hence B and E^g are conjugate in G and the result follows.

Now in the above $|H|$ and $|G/H|$ are relatively prime

and hence one of these groups has odd order. Since Feit and Thompson have shown that groups of odd order are solvable, the above result holds in general. However we will use only the result we have proved. We now obtain some applications of the above to permutation groups.

THEOREM 10.6. Let G be a permutation group and let H be a normal Hall subgroup. Let B be a complement of H and suppose that H is transitive. If either B or H is solvable then there exists a point a with $B \subseteq G_a$.

Proof. Let b be a point. Since H is transitive, $G = HG_b$. This shows that $H_b = H \cap G_b$ is a normal Hall subgroup of G_b and in fact $G_b/H_b \simeq B$. Let E be a complement of H_b in G_b. Then $H \cap E = H \cap G_b \cap E = H_b \cap E = \langle 1 \rangle$ and $HE = HH_bE = HG_b = G$ so that E is a complement of H in G. By the preceeding theorem there exists $g \in G$ with $E^g = B$. Hence $B \subseteq {G_b}^g = G_a$ where $bg = a$. This completes the proof.

COROLLARY 10.7. Let G be a primitive permutation group and suppose that G_a is a Hall subgroup. Let N be a regular normal subgroup and suppose that either G_a or N is solvable. Then N is an elementary abelian p-group.

Proof. We have $G = G_a N$ and $N \cap G_a = \langle 1 \rangle$ and hence N is also a Hall subgroup of G. Let P be a Sylow p-subgroup of N and hence of G. Then G permutes the conjugates of P and N acts transitively. By the preceeding theorem G_a normalizes one such Sylow p-subgroup, say P. Let Q be a characteristic elementary abelian subgroup of P so that G_a normalizes Q. Hence $G_a Q$ is a subgroup of G containing G_a. Since G is primitive, G_a is maximal and hence $G_a Q = G$. This yields clearly $N = Q$ and the result follows.

11. SOLVABLE GROUPS

In this section we introduce some tools for studying the structure of solvable groups. The first result is a generalization of the Sylow theorems due to P. Hall.

Let π be a set of primes. A π-number is a number whose prime factors are all contained in π. A π'-number is a number whose prime factors are all not contained in π. We say H is an S_π subgroup of G if $|H|$ is a π-number and $[G:H]$ is a π'-number. Thus H is also a Hall subgroup. K is a π-subgroup if $|K|$ is a π-number.

We consider the following statements about a group G.

E_π: G has an S_π subgroup.

C_π: G has an S_π subgroup and any two such subgroups are conjugate.

D_π: G satisfies C_π and every π-subgroup of G is contained in an S_π subgroup.

The Sylow theorems guarantee that G satisfies D_π if $\pi = \{p\}$. We show now

THEOREM 11.1. (P. Hall) Let G be a solvable group. Then for all π, G satisfies D_π.

Proof. Let K be a π-subgroup of G. We show by induction on $|G|$ that K is contained in an S_{π} subgroup of G. This will yield all but the conjugacy part of the result. Let U be a minimal normal subgroup of G. Since G is solvable U is a p-group for some prime p. Then KU/U is a π-subgroup of G/U and we can extend this to L/U an S_{π} subgroup of G/U. Then $[G:L]$ is a π'-number and $[L:U]$ is a π-number. If $p \in \pi$ then L is an S_{π} subgroup and so the result follows. Let $p \notin \pi$ so that U is a normal Hall subgroup of L. By Theorem 10.4, U has a complement S in L and clearly S is an S_{π} subgroup of G. Now K and $S \cap KU$ are both complements for U in KU. Since U is solvable Theorem 10.5 yields $K = (S \cap KU)^g$ and hence $K \subseteq S^g$, an S_{π} subgroup of G.

We now prove the conjugacy result by induction on $|G|$. Let S and T be two S_{π} subgroups of G. Let $U \neq \langle 1 \rangle$ be a normal p-subgroup of G. By induction SU/U and TU/U are conjugate in G/U and hence for some $g \in G$, $T^g \subseteq SU$. If $p \in \pi$, then $|SU|$ is a π-number and hence $SU = S$ so $T^g = S$. If $p \notin \pi$, then U is a normal Hall subgroup of SU and S and T^g are two complements. By

Theorem 10.5, $S = (T^g)^h$ and the result follows.

The converse of the above is also true. Namely if G satisfies E_π for all sets π, then G is solvable. The proof is difficult since as a first step we must show that a $\{p, q\}$-group is solvable. Hence we will not consider it here.

We state a few well known properties of nilpotent groups which we will need later.

LEMMA 11.2. Let G be a nilpotent group.

i. If $N \triangle G$, $N \neq \langle 1 \rangle$ then $N \cap \mathfrak{z}(G) \neq \langle 1 \rangle$.

ii. Let H be a group with central subgroup K. If $H/K \simeq G$, then H is nilpotent.

Proof. (i) Since a minimal normal subgroup of G is a p-group it clearly suffices to assume that G is a p-group. Let $J \subseteq N$ with $J \triangle G$ and $|J| = p$. J exists by basic properties of G. Now G permutes the elements of $J^{\#}$ and $|J^{\#}| = p-1$ so all orbits have size 1 and $J \subseteq N \cap \mathfrak{z}(G)$.

(ii) Since $\mathfrak{z}(H) \supseteq K$ we see that $H/\mathfrak{z}(H)$ is nilpotent. Thus the upper central series of H terminates at H and

H is nilpotent.

PROPOSITION 11.3. Let N and M be two normal nilpotent subgroups of G. Then NM is nilpotent.

Proof. By induction on $|G|$. Set $H = NM$. If $N \cap M = \langle 1 \rangle$ then $H = N \times M$ is clearly nilpotent so assume that $K = N \cap M \neq \langle 1 \rangle$. Now $K \triangle N$ so by the above $K \cap \mathfrak{Z}(N) \neq \langle 1 \rangle$. Clearly $K \cap \mathfrak{Z}(N) \triangle G$ so again $(K \cap \mathfrak{Z}(N)) \cap \mathfrak{Z}(M) \neq \langle 1 \rangle$. Hence $K \cap \mathfrak{Z}(H) \neq \langle 1 \rangle$. Since $K \cap \mathfrak{Z}(H) \triangle G$ we have $H/(K \cap \mathfrak{Z}(H)) = (N/(K \cap \mathfrak{Z}(H)))(M/(K \cap \mathfrak{Z}(H)))$ is nilpotent by induction. Hence the result follows by Lemma 11.2 (ii).

This says that the property of being nilpotent is normally persistent. Since G is finite, it therefore has a maximal normal nilpotent subgroup. This is called the Fitting subgroup of G and denoted by Fit G.

THEOREM 11.4. (Fitting) Let G be solvable. Then $\mathfrak{C}_G(\text{Fit } G) = \mathfrak{Z}(\text{Fit } G)$.

Proof. This is of course equivalent to $\mathcal{L}_G(\text{Fit } G) \subseteq \text{Fit } G$ which is what we show by induction on $|G|$. We can suppose that $G \neq \langle 1 \rangle$. Since G is solvable we have $F = \text{Fit } G \neq \langle 1 \rangle$. Let $Z = \mathfrak{Z}(F)$ and let $N = \mathcal{L}_G(Z)$. Thus $N \Delta G$ and $N \supseteq F$. Hence $\text{Fit } N \supseteq F$. But $\text{Fit } N$ is nilpotent and being characteristic in N, it is normal in G. This yields $\text{Fit } N \subseteq F$ and hence $F = \text{Fit } N$. Since clearly $\mathcal{L}_G(F) \subseteq \mathcal{L}_G(Z) = N$, the result will follow by induction if $N \neq G$. Thus we can assume that $N = G$ and so $Z = \mathfrak{Z}(G)$.

Let $L/Z = \text{Fit } G/Z$. Then $L \Delta G$ and by Lemma 11.2 (ii) L is nilpotent. Hence $L \subseteq F$. On the other hand F/Z is a normal nilpotent subgroup of G/Z so $F \subseteq L$ and thus $F = L$ and $\text{Fit } G/Z = F/Z$. Clearly $\mathcal{L}_G(F)/Z \subseteq \mathcal{L}_{G/Z}(F/Z)$ and by induction $\mathcal{L}_{G/Z}(F/Z) \subseteq F/Z$ so the result follows.

The above is obviously false without some assumption like solvability. For example if G is a nonabelian simple group then $\text{Fit } G = \langle 1 \rangle$ and $\mathcal{L}(\text{Fit } G) = G$. Another interesting characteristic subgroup of G is the Frattini subgroup written $\text{Fr } G$. It is defined to be the intersection of all maximal subgroups of G.

PROPOSITION 11.5. $\mathrm{Fr}\, G$ is nilpotent and hence we have $\mathrm{Fr}\, G \subseteq \mathrm{Fit}\, G$.

Proof. Let P be a Sylow p-subgroup of $\mathrm{Fr}\, G$. Now $\mathrm{Fr}\, G \triangle G$ so G permutes the Sylow p-subgroups of $\mathrm{Fr}\, G$ by conjugation. Since $\mathrm{Fr}\, G$ acts transitively we have $G = \mathcal{N}(P)\, \mathrm{Fr}\, G$. If $\mathcal{N}(P) \neq G$ then there exists a maximal subgroup M of G with $M \supseteq \mathcal{N}(P)$. Since $M \supseteq \mathrm{Fr}\, G$ this yields $M \supseteq \mathcal{N}(P)\, \mathrm{Fr}\, G = G$, a contradiction. Hence $P \triangle G$ and so $P \triangle \mathrm{Fr}\, G$ and $\mathrm{Fr}\, G$ is nilpotent.

The Frattini subgroup is most useful in the study of p-groups.

THEOREM 11.6. (Burnside Basis Theorem) Let G be a p-group and let $H = G/\mathrm{Fr}\, G$. Then H is an elementary abelian p-group. Also elements $x_1, x_2, \ldots, x_s \in G$ generate G if and only if their images in H contain a basis of H. Thus if $|H| = p^r$ then all minimal generating sets of G have size r.

<u>Proof</u>. Let M be a maximal subgroup of G. Then $M \triangle G$ and $|G/M| = p$. Thus M contains all commutators and p^{th} powers of elements of G. Hence the same is true of $\mathrm{Fr}\, G$ and so $H = G/\mathrm{Fr}\, G$ is elementary abelian.

Let $x_1, x_2, \ldots, x_s \in G$. If these elements generate G then their images in H certainly generate H and hence a subset of these images forms a basis of H. Conversely suppose the images of the x_i in H contain a basis. This yields in G, $\langle x_1, x_2, \ldots, x_s \rangle \mathrm{Fr}\, G = G$. If $\langle x_1, \ldots, x_s \rangle \neq G$ then we can find a maximal subgroup M with $M \supseteq \langle x_1, \ldots, x_s \rangle$. Since $M \geq \mathrm{Fr}\, G$ this yields $M \geq \langle x_1, \ldots, x_s \rangle \mathrm{Fr}\, G = G$, a contradiction. Finally if $|H| = p^r$ then a basis of H has size r and hence the result follows.

As an application of the above we have

THEOREM 11.7. (P. Hall) Let G be a p-group and let α be an automorphism of G of order prime to p. If the restriction of α to the quotient $G/\mathrm{Fr}\, G$ is the identity (that is, α fixes this quotient elementwise) then $\alpha = 1$.

Proof. It suffices to assume that α has prime order $q \neq p$ and to derive a contradiction. Let $x_1, \ldots, x_r$ be a minimal generating set of G. Since α fixes $G/\mathrm{Fr}\, G$ it follows that for each i, $\langle\alpha\rangle$ permutes the elements in the coset $(\mathrm{Fr}\, G)x_i$. Since $|\langle\alpha\rangle| = q$ and $|(\mathrm{Fr}\, G)x_i|$ is a power of p we see that there exists $y_i \in (\mathrm{Fr}\, G)x_i$ with $y_i\alpha = y_i$. Since the image of x_i and y_i in $G/\mathrm{Fr}\, G$ are the same, it follows by the above that $G = \langle y_1, \ldots, y_r\rangle$. Hence α fixes G, a contradiction.

12. TRANSFER THEOREMS

The transfer is a technique which allows us to translate properties of subgroups of G into homomorphisms of G.

Let G be a group and H a subgroup. Let $x_1, \ldots, x_n$ be right coset representatives of H in G. Then G permutes these right cosets by right multiplication. Let $g \in G$ and say $Hx_ig = Hx_{i'}$. Then $x_ig = h_ix_{i'}$ for some $h_i \in H$. Define $V_{G\to H}(g) \equiv \prod_i h_i \mod H'$. Thus $V_{G\to H}$

is a map from G into H/H'. It is called the transfer of G into H. Its basic properties are

THEOREM 12.1. $V_{G \to H}$ is a homomorphism of G into H/H'. The map is independent of the choice of coset representatives of H.

Proof. Let $f, g \in G$ and say $x_i f = h_i x_{i'}$ and $x_i g = k_i x_{i^*}$ with $h_i, k_i \in H$. Then $x_i fg = h_i x_{i'} g = h_i k_{i'} x_{i'^*}$.

Hence

$$V_{G \to H}(fg) \equiv \prod (h_i k_{i'}) \equiv (\prod h_i)(\prod k_i) \mod H'$$

and so $V_{G \to H}(fg) = V_{G \to H}(f)\, V_{G \to H}(g)$. This yields the first result.

Now let $x_i g = h_i x_{i'}$. Suppose $y_1, \ldots, y_n$ is another set of coset representatives of H with $y_i = k_i x_i$ for $k_i \in H$. Then $y_i g = k_i x_i g = k_i h_i x_{i'} = k_i h_i k_{i'}^{-1} y_{i'}$. Since clearly $\prod (k_i h_i k_{i'}^{-1}) \equiv \prod h_i \mod H'$ the result follows.

The fact that transfer is independent of the choice of coset representative allows us a good deal of freedom. This is evident in the proof of the following.

PROPOSITION 12.2. Let H be a subgroup of G and let L be a normal subgroup of H. Suppose H/L is abelian of order $m > 1$ with $(m, n) = 1$ where $[G:H] = n$. Let g be a fixed element of $H-L$ with the property that for all integers r and for all $x \in G$, if $(g^r)^x \in H$ then $(g^r)^x \equiv g^r \mod L$. Then G has a normal subgroup K with $G > K$ and $|G/K| \mid |H/H'|$.

Proof. Let K be the kernel of the homomorphism $V_{G \to H}$. Then certainly $|G/K| \mid |H/H'|$. We need only show that $K \neq G$ and we do this by showing that $g \notin K$. Now G permutes the right cosets of H by right multiplication. Suppose under this action g has cycles of length $r_1, r_2, \ldots, r$ where of course $r_1 + r_2 + \ldots + r_t = n$. Consider a typical cycle of length r and suppose that it contains the point Hx. Then take for the remaining coset representatives of cosets in this cycle the elements $xg, xg^2, \ldots, xg^{r-1}$. Since $xg^r \in Hx$ we see that the contribution of this cycle to $V_{G \to H}(g)$ is

$xg^r x^{-1}$. Hence if Hx_i is in the ith cycle of g we have $V_{G\to H}(g) \equiv \prod (x_i g^{r_i} x_i^{-1})$ mod H'. If $V_{G\to H}(g) = 1$, then $\prod(x_i g^{r_i} x_i^{-1}) \in H'$ and hence $\prod(x_i g^{r_i} x_i^{-1}) \in L$ since $L \supseteq H'$ by assumption. Now $x_i g^{r_i} x_i^{-1} \in H$ so again by assumption $x_i g^{r_i} x_i^{-1} \equiv g^{r_i}$ mod L. Thus $\prod g^{r_i} = g^n \in L$. Since n is prime to H/L this implies that $g \in L$, a contradiction. This completes the proof.

The above result has many consequences. One such of a special nature is

PROPOSITION 12.3. Let G be a group with no subgroup of index 2 and let Q be a Sylow 2-subgroup of G. Suppose that Q has a cyclic subgroup A of index 2. Then all elements of G of order 2 are conjugate. If further Q is a quaternion group then all elements of G of order 4 are conjugate.

Proof. By Sylow's theorem it suffices to show that all elements of Q of the appropriate order are conjugate in G. Now all elements of A of the appropriate order are in fact conjugate in Q since if the order is 2 then there is only one such element and if Q is the quaternion group and the order is 4 then this is known. Let $g \in Q - A$ be an element of the appropriate order. We apply the preceeding result with $H = Q$, $L = A$. Since G has no subgroup of index 2 we see that there exists an integer r and $x \in G$ with $(g^r)^x \in Q$ but $(g^r)^x \not\equiv g^r \mod A$. Say $o(g) = 2$. Then certainly $r = 1$ and hence $g^x \not\equiv g \mod A$. Thus $g^x \in A$ and so g belongs to the class of the unique element of A of order 2. If $o(g) = 4$ then Q is a quaternion group. If $r = 2$ then g^2 and $(g^2)^x$ would both have to be the unique element of Q of order 2, a contradiction. Hence we must have $r = \pm 1$. If $r = -1$ then by taking inverses we can assume $r = 1$. Hence $g^x \in A$ and g belongs to the class of the elements of A of order 4. This completes the proof.

For more general results we introduce the following terminology. If $H \subseteq G$ we define the focal subgroup of H in G to be $\mathrm{Foc}_G(H)$ the subgroup generated by all the commutators (h, g) with $h \in H$, $g \in G$ and $(h, g) \in H$. Hence clearly $H' \subseteq \mathrm{Foc}_G(H) \subseteq H$. The focal series of H in

G is the series $H = H_0, H_1, \ldots$ defined by $H_{n+1} = \mathrm{Foc}_G(H_n)$. We say H is hyperfocal in G if for some n, $H_n = \langle 1 \rangle$.

We note a trivial property. Let $K \subseteq H \subseteq G$. Since $\mathrm{Foc}_G(K) \subseteq \mathrm{Foc}_G(H)$ we see that if H is hyperfocal in G then also K is hyperfocal in G. Moreover since $\mathrm{Foc}_H(K) \subseteq \mathrm{Foc}_G(K)$ we see that if K is hyperfocal in G then also K is hyperfocal in H.

Let π be a set of primes. A normal π-complement of G is a normal $S_{\pi'}$ subgroup. Clearly if this group exists it is unique and hence characteristic in G.

THEOREM 12.4. Let H be a hyperfocal S_π subgroup of G. Then G has a normal π-complement.

Proof. By induction on $|G|$. Assume $H \neq \langle 1 \rangle$. Let $L = \mathrm{Foc}_G(H)$ so that $H' \subseteq L < H$. The strict inclusion $L < H$ follows since H is hyperfocal in G. Let $g \in H - L$. If $(g^r)^x \in H$ for some integer r and $x \in G$ then $(g^r, x) = g^{-r}(g^r)^x \in H$ and hence to L. Thus $(g^r)^x \equiv g^r \mod L$. By Proposition 12.2 G has a normal subgroup $K < G$ with

G/K a π-group.

Now $H \cap K$ is an S_π subgroup of K which is hyperfocal in G and hence in K. By induction K has a normal π-complement N. Since N is characteristic in K we have $N \Delta G$. Finally since $[G:K]$ is a π-number, N is a normal π-complement of G.

COROLLARY 12.5. Let H be a nilpotent S_π subgroup of G. Suppose that any two elements of H which are conjugate in G are conjugate in H. Then G has a normal π-complement.

Proof. We show that H is hyperfocal in G. In fact we show that the focal and lower central series of H are identical. Since H is nilpotent, the result will follow by Theorem 12.4. Suppose we have already shown that $H_i = L_i$ where L_i is the ith term in the lower central series of H. Since $L_{i+1} = (H, L_i)$ we have clearly $L_{i+1} \subseteq Foc_G(H_i) = H_{i+1}$. Consider a generator y of H_{i+1}. It is of the form $y = (h, g)$ with $h \in H_i$, $g \in G$ and

$(h, g) \in H_i$. Since $(h, g) = h^{-1}h^g$ we see that $h^g \in H$. By assumption there exists $k \in H$ with $h^g = h^k$ and hence $y = (h, g) = (h, k) \in (L_i, H) = L_{i+1}$. This completes the proof.

Since p-groups are nilpotent we have

COROLLARY 12.6. Let P be a Sylow p-subgroup of G. Suppose that any two elements of P which are conjugate in G are conjugate in P. Then G has a normal p-complement.

THEOREM 12.7. (Burnside) Let P be a Sylow p-subgroup of G. If P is in the center of its normalizer then G has a normal p-complement.

Proof. Clearly P is abelian. Let $x, y \in P$ be two elements which are conjugate in G. Say $y = x^g$. Then $y \in P, P^g$ and so both P and P^g are contained in $C = \mathcal{L}(y)$. By Sylow's theorem $P^g = P^c$ with $c \in C$ and then $cg^{-1} \in \mathcal{N}(P)$. By assumption cg^{-1} centralizes y and hence $g^{-1} \in \mathcal{L}(y)$. Finally $x = y^{g^{-1}} = y$ and so certainly any two elements of P which are conjugate in G are conjugate in P. Thus the result follows by Corollary 12.6.

A Z-group is a group in which every Sylow subgroup is cyclic. An interesting application of the above is

LEMMA 12.8. If G is a Z-group, then G is solvable.

<u>Proof</u>. By induction on $|G|$. Let P be a Sylow p-subgroup of G for the smallest prime divisor of $|G|$. Let $N = \mathfrak{N}(P)$. Then N acts on P and we have a homomorphism $N \longrightarrow \mathrm{Aut}\, P$. Since P is abelian and a Sylow p-subgroup of N we see that the image is a p'-group. Now if $|P| = p^t$ then $|\mathrm{Aut}\, P| = (p-1)p^{t-1}$ and so all prime divisors of the order of this image are less than p. By the minimality of p, this image is $\langle 1 \rangle$ and P is in the center of its normalizer. By the previous result G has a normal p-complement H. Since G/H is cyclic and H is a Z-group, the result follows.

LEMMA 12.9. Let G be solvable and let π be a set of prime factors of G such that if $p \in \pi$ then the Sylow

p-subgroups of G are cyclic. Then the S_π subgroups of G' are cyclic.

Proof. By induction on the derived length of G. If G' is abelian the result is clear. Suppose that $G^{(n+1)} = \langle 1 \rangle$. By induction $(G/G^{(n)})'$ has cyclic S_π subgroups. Let $x \in G'$ be a π-element which is the inverse image of a generator of one of these cyclic groups. Now $G^{(n)}$ is abelian and hence it has a normal S_π subgroup K. Clearly K is cyclic and being characteristic in $G^{(n)}$ it is normal in G. Since the automorphism group of every cyclic p-group is abelian, it follows that Aut K is abelian. Now $K \Delta G$ and G acts on K so G' centralizes K. Hence $\langle x, K \rangle$ is an abelian S_π subgroup of G'. It is in fact cyclic since all its Sylow subgroups are cyclic. Finally G' is solvable so all S_π subgroups are conjugate and the result follows.

LEMMA 12.10. Let P be a Sylow p-subgroup of G. Suppose that P is cyclic and $P \not\subseteq G'$. Then G has a normal p-complement.

Proof. Let $N = \mathfrak{N}(P)$. Then N acts on P and the image of $N \longrightarrow \text{Aut } P$ is a p'-group. If $x \in N$ then $(P, x) \subseteq P \cap G' < P$. Thus if P_1 is the subgroup of P of index p and if $g \in P$ then $g^{-1}g^x \in P_1$ so $g^x \equiv g \mod P_1$. Hence x fixes P/P_1 and as we have shown this implies that $g^x = g$. Therefore P is in the center of its normalizer and the normal p-complement exists.

PROPOSITION 12.11. Let G be a Z-group. Then G is generated by elements x, y with $x^n = 1$, $y^m = 1$, $y^x = y^r$ and $(r-1, m) = (n, m) = 1$, $r^n \equiv 1 \mod m$.

Proof. By Lemma 12.8 G is solvable and hence by Lemma 12.9 G' is cyclic. Let π be the set of prime divisors of $|G|$ such that if $p \in \pi$ then no Sylow p-subgroup of G is contained in G'. For each prime $p \in \pi$ let U_p be the normal p-complement of G guaranteed by the preceeding lemma. It is easy to see that $U = \bigcap U_p$ is a normal π-complement of G. Also $U_p \supseteq G'$ so we have $U \supseteq G'$. If $U \neq G'$, then for some $p \mid |U|$ a Sylow p-subgroup of U would not be contained in G', a contradiction since $p \notin \pi$. Hence $U = G'$ is an $S_{\pi'}$ subgroup of G. Let $G' = \langle y \rangle$. Since an S_π subgroup of G is isomorphic to G/G', it is abelian and hence cyclic. Let x generate some S_π subgroup of G. Then certainly G is generated by x and y with $x^n = 1$, $y^m = 1$ and $(m, n) = 1$. Since $\langle y \rangle \triangle G$ we have $y^x = y^r$ for some integer r. Then $y = y^{x^n} = y^{r^n}$ so $r^n \equiv 1 \mod m$. Finally we see that $G' = \langle (y, x) \rangle = \langle y \rangle$. Since $(y, x) = y^{-1}y^x = y^{r-1}$ we must have $(r-1, m) = 1$ and the result follows.

13. NORMAL p-COMPLEMENTS

We say a group G is p-solvable if it has a normal series in which every quotient is either a p-group or a p'-group. Obviously every subgroup and quotient group of a p-solvable group is p-solvable. We let the p-length of G be the number of p-quotients in a normal series of the above type of minimal length.

Let π be a set of primes. Since the property of being a π-group is normally persistent G has a maximal normal π-subgroup which we denote by $O_{\pi}(G)$. Also $O_{\pi'}(G)$ is the maximal normal π'-subgroup of G.

If G has a normal p-complement then G is p-solvable of p-length ≤ 1. The following result is known as Lemma 1.2.3. It is the p-solvable analogue of Fitting's theorem (Theorem 11.4) for solvable groups.

PROPOSITION 13.1. (P. Hall-G. Higman) Let G be p-solvable with $O_{p'}(G) = \langle 1 \rangle$. Then $\mathcal{C}_G(O_p(G)) = \mathfrak{Z}(O_p(G))$.

Proof. We need to show that $\mathcal{C}_G(O_p(G)) \subseteq O_p(G)$ or equivalently that $H = O_p(G)\,\mathcal{C}_G(O_p(G))$ is in fact $O_p(G)$. Clearly $H \triangle G$. If $O_{p'}(H) \neq \langle 1 \rangle$ then since $O_{p'}(H)$ is characteristic in H it is normal in G and $O_{p'}(G) \supseteq O_{p'}(H) > \langle 1 \rangle$, a contradiction. Note also that since $O_p(H) \triangle G$, $O_p(H) \subseteq O_p(G)$ and hence $O_p(H) = O_p(G)$.

Suppose that $H > O_p(G)$. Then $H/O_p(G)$ is a

nonidentity p-solvable group and therefore it has a nonidentity normal p- or p'-subgroup. Since $O_p(H) = O_p(G)$, $H/O_p(G)$ cannot have a normal p-subgroup. Hence if K is the complete inverse image in H of $O_{p'}(H/O_p(G))$, then $K \triangle G$ and $K > O_p(G)$. Now $O_p(G)$ is a normal Sylow p-subgroup of K so by the Schur-Zassenhaus theorem, $O_p(G)$ has a complement L in K. Let $x \in L$. Since $L \subseteq O_p(G)\, \mathcal{L}_G(O_p(G))$ we can write $x = yz$ with $y \in O_p(G)$, $z \in \mathcal{L}_G(O_p(G))$. Then the action of x on $O_p(G)$ is the same as that of y. Since $o(x)$ and $o(y)$ are relatively prime we see that x centralizes $O_p(G)$. Hence $K = L \times O_p(G)$ and $L = O_{p'}(K) > \langle 1 \rangle$. Now $K \triangle G$ so $O_{p'}(K) \triangle G$, a contradiction.

Let p be a fixed prime. We say G is an A-group if whenever S and T are two Sylow p-subgroups of G then there exists $x \in \mathcal{L}(S \cap T)$ with $S^x = T$.

If X is a subgroup of G, we set $A(X) = A_G(X) = \mathcal{N}_G(X)/\mathcal{L}_G(X)$. That is, $A(X)$ is the group of automorphisms induced on X by G.

PROPOSITION 13.2. Let G have a normal p-complement.

Then G is an A-group. Moreover if X is any p-subgroup of G, then $A(X)$ is a p-group.

Proof. Let N be the normal p-complement of G and let S and T be two Sylow p-subgroups of G. Then S and T are conjugate in G. Since $G = SN$ we can find $y \in N$ with $S^y = T$. Let $s \in S \cap T$. Then $s \in T$ and $s^y \in T$ so $(s, y) = s^{-1}s^y \in T$. Since $N \triangle G$, $(s, y) \in N$. Hence $(s, y) = 1$ and y centralizes $S \cap T$.

Let X be a p-subgroup of G and let $M = \mathcal{N}(X)$. Then $M \cap N$ is a normal p-complement of M. If $x \in X$, $y \in M \cap N$ then $(x, y) \in X \cap (M \cap N) = \langle 1 \rangle$. Hence y centralizes X and $\mathcal{C}(X) \supseteq M \cap N$. Thus $A(X)$ is a p-group.

The converse of the second part of the above is due to Frobenius. The proof below is due to G. Higman. It is longer but more transparent than the original one.

THEOREM 13.3. (Frobenius) Let G be a group with the property that if X is any p-subgroup then $A_G(X)$ is a p-group. Then G has a normal p-complement.

<u>Proof</u>. Let G be a minimal counterexample.

<u>Step 1</u>. If $H < G$ then H has a normal p-complement.

Let X be a p-subgroup of H. Then we have $A_H(X) = \mathcal{N}_H(X)/\mathcal{L}_H(X) = (\mathcal{N}_G(X) \cap H)/(\mathcal{L}_G(X) \cap H)$ and the latter group is canonically embedded in $A_G(X)$. Hence H satisfies the hypothesis of the theorem and by the minimality of G, H has a normal p-complement.

<u>Step 2</u>. $O_p(G) = \langle 1 \rangle$.

Let $K = O_p(G)$ and let X/K be a p-subgroup of G/K. Then X is a p-subgroup of G. Under the combined map $\mathcal{N}_G(X) \to \mathcal{N}_{G/K}(X/K) \to \mathcal{N}_{G/K}(X/K)/\mathcal{L}_{G/K}(X/K)$ the subgroup $\mathcal{L}_G(X)$ maps into $\langle 1 \rangle$. Hence this induces an epimorphism $A_G(X) \to A_{G/K}(X/K)$ and so the latter group is a p-group. If $K \neq \langle 1 \rangle$ then by the minimality of G, G/K has a normal p-complement M/K. Here $M \triangle G$ and G/M is a p-group. Also K is a normal Sylow p-subgroup of M. By the Schur-Zassenhaus theorem, K has a complement L in M.

Now L normalizes K, L is a p'-group and $A_G(K)$ is a p-group. Thus L centralizes K and $M = L \times K$.

Since $L = O_{p'}(M)$ and $M \Delta G$ we have $L \Delta G$. Clearly L is a normal p-complement of G, a contradiction.

Step 3. G is an A-group.

Let P and P_1 be two Sylow p-subgroups. We prove the result by induction on $[P:P \cap P_1] = [P_1:P \cap P_1]$. The result is certainly true if this index is 1. Also if $P \cap P_1 = \langle 1 \rangle$ then $\mathcal{L}_G(P \cap P_1) = G$ and the result follows by Sylow's theorem. Hence we can assume that $P \cap P_1 \neq \langle 1 \rangle$. Set $H = \mathcal{N}_G(P \cap P_1)$. Since $O_p(G) = \langle 1 \rangle$ it follows that $H \neq G$ and thus H has a normal p-complement.

We use the basic fact that if Q is a proper subgroup of P then $\mathcal{N}_P(Q) > Q$. Hence $H \cap P > P \cap P_1$ and $H \cap P_1 > P \cap P_1$ since by assumption $P \neq P_1$. Let R be a

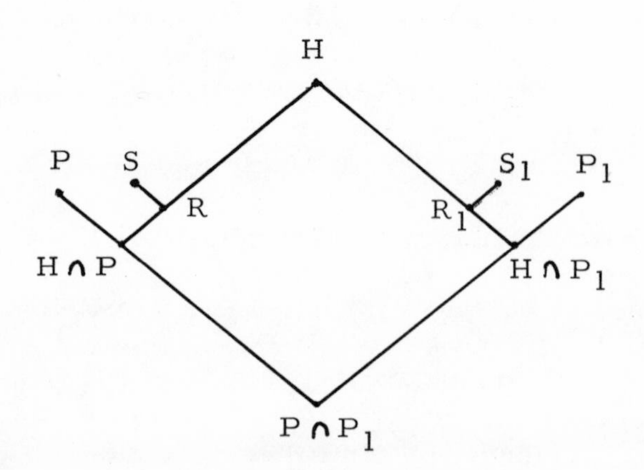

Sylow p-subgroup of H with $R \supseteq H \cap P$ and let R_1 be another with $R_1 \supseteq H \cap P_1$. By Proposition 13.2 H is an A-group and hence there exists $y \in \mathcal{L}_H(R \cap R_1)$ with $R_1 = R^y$. Let S be a Sylow p-subgroup of G with $S \supseteq R$ and set $S_1 = S^y$ so that $S_1 \supseteq R_1$. Now $P \cap S > P \cap P_1$ and $P_1 \cap S_1 > P \cap P_1$ so by induction there exists $u \in \mathcal{L}_G(S \cap P)$ and $v \in \mathcal{L}_G(S_1 \cap P_1)$ with $P^u = S$ and $S_1{}^v = P_1$. Hence $P^{uyv} = P_1$. Since $R \cap R_1$, $S \cap P$ and $S_1 \cap P_1$ all contain $P \cap P_1$ we see that $uyv \in \mathcal{L}(P \cap P_1)$ and the result follows.

Step 4. Contradiction.

Let P be a Sylow p-subgroup of G. Let $g, h \in P$ be elements conjugate in G. Say $h = g^x$ so that $h \in P \cap P^x$. Since G is an A-group then exists $y \in \mathcal{L}(P \cap P^x)$ with $P^{xy} = P$. Note that $h^y = h$. Now $xy \in \mathcal{N}(P) = \mathcal{L}(P)\, P$ since $A_G(P)$ is a p-group. Hence $xy = uv$ with $u \in \mathcal{L}(P)$, $v \in P$. Then $g^v = g^{uv} = g^{xy} = h^y = h$. This says that any two elements of P conjugate in G are conjugate in P. By Corollary 12.6 G has a normal p-complement, a contradiction. This completes the proof of the theorem.

As an application we prove

PROPOSITION 13.4. Let G be a group with no normal 2-complement. Let Q be a Sylow 2-subgroup of G and suppose that Q has a cyclic subgroup A of index 2. Then $3 \mid |G|$.

Proof. By the preceeding theorem, since G does not have a normal 2-complement, there exists a subgroup X of Q with $\mathfrak{N}(X)/\mathfrak{L}(X)$ not a 2-group. Then $A \cap X$ is a cyclic subgroup of X of index 1 or 2 and hence X has two generators. Now there exists $g \in \mathfrak{N}(X)/\mathfrak{L}(X)$ an element of order q, for some prime $q \neq 2$, which acts faithfully on X and hence on $X/\mathrm{Fr}\, X$ by Theorem 11.7. Since X has two generators the Burnside Basis Theorem yields $|X/\mathrm{Fr}\, X| \leq 4$. This clearly yields $q = 3$ and the result follows.

It is not true that if G is an A-group, then G has a normal p-complement. For example, if G is a nonabelian simple group with a Sylow p-subgroup P of order p, then certainly G is an A-group. It is convenient at this time to consider concrete examples of such groups.

Let p be a prime and let $GL(2,p)$ denote the group

of nonsingular 2×2 matrices over $GF(p)$, the field with p elements. In addition we let $SL(2,p)$ be the subgroup of $GL(2,p)$ consisting of all those matrices of determinant 1 and we let $PSL(2,p) = SL(2,p)/\mathfrak{Z}(SL(2,p))$. Here "GL" stands for "general linear", "SL" for "special linear" and "PSL" for "projective special linear". Some basic properties of these groups are tabulated below.

PROPOSITION 13.5. Let p be an odd prime.

i. $SL(2,p) \trianglelefteq GL(2,p)$

$|GL(2,p)| = (p-1)^2 p(p+1)$

$|SL(2,p)| = (p-1)p(p+1)$

$|PSL(2,p)| = (p-1)p(p+1)/2$.

ii. If P_1 and P_2 are two distinct subgroups of $SL(2,p)$ of order p, then $\langle P_1, P_2 \rangle = SL(2,p)$.

iii. Let N be a p'-subgroup of $SL(2,p)$ and let $|P| = p$. If P normalizes but does not centralize N, then $p = 3$ and N is nonabelian.

iv. $PSL(2,p)$ is a nonabelian simple group for $p \geq 5$.

v. The Sylow 2-subgroups of $SL(2,p)$ are

quaternion groups.

Proof. (i) We count $|GL(2,p)|$. Let $\begin{bmatrix} a & b \\ c & d \end{bmatrix} \in GL(2,p)$.

Now there are p^2-1 choices for the first row since $a = b = 0$ cannot occur. Once this first row is given there are p^2-p choices for the second row since we need only delete $c = \lambda a$, $d = \lambda b$ for all $\lambda \in GF(p)$. Hence we have $|GL(2,p)| = (p^2-1)(p^2-p)$. The determinant map is a homomorphism of $GL(2,p)$ into the multiplicative group of $GF(p)$. Since $\det \begin{bmatrix} a & 0 \\ 0 & 1 \end{bmatrix} = a$, the map is onto. Since $SL(2,p)$ is the kernel we have $SL(2,p) \triangle GL(2,p)$ and $[GL(2,p):SL(2,p)] = p-1$.

For the remainder of this proof we set $G = SL(2,p)$. We see that every Sylow p-subgroup of G has order p. Set $P = \left\{\begin{bmatrix} 1 & 0 \\ a & 1 \end{bmatrix}\right\}$ and $P_1 = \left\{\begin{bmatrix} 1 & a \\ 0 & 1 \end{bmatrix}\right\}$. It is easy to see that both these sets are in fact subgroups of G of order p and hence are Sylow p-subgroups of G. It is also easy to see that $\mathfrak{N}_G(P) = \left\{\begin{bmatrix} b & 0 \\ a & b^{-1} \end{bmatrix}\right\}$ and $\mathfrak{C}_G(P)$ is the subgroup of $\mathfrak{N}_G(P)$ with $b = \pm 1$. The symmetric result holds for P_1.

This implies since $\mathfrak{Z}(G) \subseteq \mathcal{L}_G(P) \cap \mathcal{L}_G(P_1)$ that $\mathfrak{Z}(G) = \left\{ \pm \begin{bmatrix} 1 & 0 \\ 0 & 1 \end{bmatrix} \right\}$. Hence since $p > 2$, $|\mathfrak{Z}(G)| = 2$ and (i) follows.

The above also yields $|\mathcal{N}_G(P)| = p(p-1)$ and $|\mathcal{L}_G(P)| = 2p$. Hence $|A_G(P)| = (p-1)/2$ and thus if $p > 3$ then G does not have a normal p-complement by Proposition 13.2. Since $[G:\mathcal{N}_G(P)] = p+1$, G has $p+1$ distinct Sylow p-subgroups.

(ii) Let H be a subgroup of G generated by two subgroups of order p. By Sylow's theorem, H must contain at least $p+1$ such subgroups and hence $H \supseteq \langle P, P_1 \rangle$. It therefore suffices to show that $\langle P, P_1 \rangle = G$. Let $x = \begin{bmatrix} a & b \\ c & d \end{bmatrix} \in G$. If $c = 0$ then $a \neq 0$ and

$$\begin{bmatrix} a & b \\ a & b+d \end{bmatrix} = \begin{bmatrix} 1 & 0 \\ 1 & 1 \end{bmatrix} \begin{bmatrix} a & b \\ c & d \end{bmatrix}$$

is a matrix with (2, 1) element not zero. Since $\begin{bmatrix} 1 & 0 \\ 1 & 1 \end{bmatrix} \in P$, it suffices to show that $x \in \langle P, P_1 \rangle$ under the assumption that $c \neq 0$. Set $\lambda = (1-a)/c$. Then we see easily that

$$\begin{bmatrix} 1 & 0 \\ -c & 1 \end{bmatrix} \begin{bmatrix} 1 & \lambda \\ 0 & 1 \end{bmatrix} \begin{bmatrix} a & b \\ c & d \end{bmatrix} = \begin{bmatrix} 1 & e \\ 0 & f \end{bmatrix}$$

for suitable field elements e and f. Since the determinant of the right hand element is 1 we have $f = 1$ and thus $\begin{bmatrix} 1 & e \\ 0 & f \end{bmatrix} \in P_1$. This clearly proves (ii).

(iii) Let N and P be given. If N normalizes P then $(N, P) \subseteq N \cap P = \langle 1 \rangle$, a contradiction. Hence the group NP contains two subgroups of order p. By (ii), $NP = G$ and then clearly N is a normal p-complement. As we have seen above this implies that $p = 3$ and then N is clearly a Sylow 2-subgroup of G. If $p = 3$ and

$$x = \begin{bmatrix} 0 & 1 \\ -1 & 0 \end{bmatrix} \qquad y = \begin{bmatrix} 1 & 1 \\ 1 & -1 \end{bmatrix}$$

then $x, y \in G$, $y^4 = 1$, $x^2 = y^2$ and $x^{-1}yx = y^{-1}$ so a Sylow 2-subgroup of $SL(2, 3)$ contains the quaternion group of order 8.

(iv) Let $N \triangle G$ with $N \neq G$. If $p \mid |N|$, then N contains all subgroups of G of order p, a contradiction by (ii). Thus N is a p'-group. Let P have order p in G. Then P normalizes N. Since $p > 3$, (iii) implies that

P centralizes N. Hence N is a p'-subgroup of $\mathcal{L}_G(P)$ and from the structure of the latter group we see that $N \subseteq \mathfrak{Z}(G)$. This shows that for $p > 3$, PSL(2, p) is simple. It is nonabelian since its order $p(p+1)(p-1)/2$ cannot be a prime.

(v) Let $g \in G$ have order 2. Since g has determinant 1 its characteristic polynomial is x^2+ax+1 for some field element a. However $g^2 = 1$ so g also is a root of $x^2-1 = (x-1)(x+1)$. By subtracting the two, g satisfies $ax+2 = 0$. Since $ax+2$ must divide x^2-1 we see that g satisfies $x-1 = 0$ or $x+1 = 0$. Thus since $g \neq 1$ we must have $g = -1$ or rather $g = \begin{bmatrix} -1 & 0 \\ 0 & -1 \end{bmatrix}$. This shows that G has a unique element of order 2 and the same is therefore true for Q, a Sylow 2-subgroup of G. Hence Q is either cyclic or quaternion. If $p = 3$, then Q is not cyclic by the above. If $p > 3$, then since PSL(2, p) is simple and of even order, it follows by Theorem 12.7 that the Sylow 2-subgroup of PSL(2, p) cannot be cyclic. Hence Q is quaternion and the proposition is proved.

SL(2, 5), a group of order 120, plays a special role

in the study of Frobenius complements. We consider this group now.

LEMMA 13.6. $\mathrm{Alt}(5) = \mathrm{gp}\langle x, y \mid x^3 = 1,\ y^5 = 1,\ (xy)^2 = 1\rangle$.

<u>Proof.</u> Let G be the right hand group. Let $a, b \in \mathrm{Alt}(5)$ with $a = (4\ 2\ 1)$, $b = (1\ 2\ 3\ 4\ 5)$. Then $a^3 = 1$, $b^5 = 1$ and $ab = (1\ 5)(3\ 4)$ so $(ab)^2 = 1$. If $L = \langle a, b\rangle$ then we see that $2, 3, 5 \mid |L|$ so $|L| = 30$ or 60. Since $\mathrm{Alt}(5)$ is simple, $|L| \neq 30$ and hence $\mathrm{Alt}(5) = \langle a, b\rangle$. Thus there is an obvious homomorphism of G onto $\mathrm{Alt}(5)$. It suffices now to show that G is finite and to suitably bound $|G|$.

Set $H = \langle y\rangle$ so that $|H| \leq 5$ and define twelve cosets of H by

$$
\begin{array}{lll}
H_1 = H & H_2 = Hx & H_3 = Hx^2 \\
H_4 = Hx^2y & H_5 = Hx^2yx & H_6 = Hx^2yx^2 \\
H_7 = Hx^2y^2 & H_8 = Hx^2y^2x & H_9 = Hx^2y^2x^2 \\
H_{10} = Hx^2y^2x^2y & H_{11} = Hx^2y^2x^2yx & H_{12} = Hx^2y^2x^2yx^2 .
\end{array}
$$

Note that these are not necessarily distinct. Set $K = \bigcup H_i$.

We show that $Kx = Ky = K$. Since $x^3 = 1$ it is clear that $Kx = K$.

From $(xy)^2 = 1$ we obtain easily $yxy = x^2$, $y^4x^2 = xy$ and $x^2y^4 = yx$. Now

$$H_1y = Hy = H = H_1$$

$$H_2y = Hxy = Hy^4x^2 = Hx^2 = H_3$$

$$H_3y = Hx^2y = H_4$$

$$H_4y = Hx^2y^2 = H_7$$

$$H_5y = Hx^2(yxy) = Hx^4 = Hx = H_2$$

$$H_6y = Hx^2(yx)xy = Hx^2x^2y^4xy = Hxy^4xy = H(yxy)y^3xy$$

$$= Hx^2y^3xy = Hx^2y^2(yxy) = Hx^2y^2x^2 = H_9$$

$$H_7y = Hx^2y^3 = H(x^2y^4)y^4 = Hyxy^4 = Hxy^4 = Hx^2(x^2y^4)$$

$$= Hx^2yx = H_5$$

$$H_8y = Hx^2y(yxy) = Hx^2yx^2 = H_6$$

$$H_9y = Hx^2y^2x^2y = H_{10}$$

$$H_{10}y = Hx^2y^2x^2y^2 = H(x^2y^4)y^3x^2y^2 = Hyxy^3x^2y^2$$

$$= Hxy^3x^2y^2 = Hx^2(x^2y^4)(y^4x^2)y^2 = Hx^2yx^2y^3$$

$$= Hx^2y(x^2y^4)y^4 = Hx^2y^2xy^4 = Hx^2y^2x^2(x^2y^4)$$

$$= Hx^2y^2x^2yx = H_{11}$$

$$H_{11}y = Hx^2y^2x^2(yxy) = Hx^2y^2x = H_8$$

$$H_{12}y = Hx^2y^2x^2(yx)xy = Hx^2y^2x^2x^2y^4xy = Hx^2y(yx)y^4xy$$
$$= Hx^2yx^2y^3xy = Hx^2(yx)xy^3xy = Hxy^4xy^3xy$$
$$= H(yx)y^4xy^3xy = Hx^2y^3xy^3xy = Hx^2y^2(yxy)y^2xy$$
$$= Hx^2y^2x^2y^2xy = Hx^2y^2x^2y(yxy) = Hx^2y^2x^2yx^2 = H_{12}.$$

This yields $Kx = Ky = K$ and hence $KG = K$. Therefore $G = K$ and since $|K| \leq 12\,|H| \leq 60$ we have $|G| \leq 60$ and the result follows.

PROPOSITION 13.7. $SL(2,5)$ is the unique nonsolvable group of order 120 with quaternion Sylow 2-subgroup. Moreover $SL(2,5) = gp\langle x, y, z \mid x^3 = y^5 = z^2 = 1,\ x^z = x,\ y^z = y,\ (xy)^2 = z\rangle$.

Proof. By Proposition 13.5, $SL(2,5)$ has the first properties mentioned. Now let G be any such group and let Q be a Sylow 2-subgroup. Then Q is quaternion of order 8. Set $H = \mathfrak{N}(Q)$. If $X < Q$, then X is cyclic so Aut X is a 2-group. If $A_G(Q)$ is a 2-group then by Theorem 13.3 G has a normal 2-complement N. Then $|N| = 15$ so N is solvable and G is solvable, a contradiction.

Since $|\text{Aut } Q| = 24$, it follows that $3 \mid [H:\mathcal{L}(Q)]$. In particular $24 \mid |H|$. If $|H| > 24$, then $H = G$ and $|G/Q| = 15$. Hence again G is solvable, a contradiction. Thus $|H| = 24$ and in fact $H = QJ$ where $|J| = 3$ and J normalizes but does not centralize Q.

Now $[G:H] = 5$ and G permutes the right cosets of H by right multiplication and in this way we have a homomorphism of G into Sym(5). Let K be the kernel so that $K \Delta G$ and $K \subseteq H$. Now $K \neq H$ since otherwise G is solvable. Also $K \neq \langle 1 \rangle$ since otherwise $G \simeq \text{Sym}(5)$ by order considerations and this is a contradiction since Sym(5) has dihedral Sylow 2-subgroups. Also $K \neq Q$ since Q is not normal in G. Now $K \subseteq H$ and $K \Delta H$ so from the structure of H we see that the only remaining possibility is $|K| = 2$. Hence K is central in G and G/K is a subgroup of Sym(5) of index 2. Thus $G/K \simeq \text{Alt}(5)$. Let $K = \langle c \rangle$. By the preceeding lemma it is clear that we can find $a, b \in G$ with $G = \langle a, b, c \rangle$ and $a^3 = 1$, $b^5 = 1$, $ab \notin \langle c \rangle$, $(ab)^2 \in \langle c \rangle$. Since the Sylow 2-subgroups of G are quaternion we must have $(ab)^2 = c$.

Let $L = \text{gp}\langle x, y, z \mid x^3 = y^5 = z^2 = 1,\ x^z = x,\ y^z = y,$

$(xy)^2 = z\rangle$. By the above there is an obvious homomorphism of L onto G. We show that $|L| \leq 120$. Set $Z = \langle z \rangle$ so that Z is a central subgroup of L and $|Z| \leq 2$. Moreover L/Z is generated by two elements $\bar{x}, \bar{y}$ with $\bar{x}^3 = \bar{y}^5 = (\bar{x}\,\bar{y})^2 = 1$. Hence L/Z is a homomorphic image of $\mathrm{gp}\langle x, y \mid x^3 = y^5 = 1, (xy)^2 = 1\rangle$, a group of order 60 by the previous lemma. Thus $|L| \leq 120$. This yields $|L| = 120$ and $L \cong G$. Therefore G is unique up to isomorphism and so $G \cong SL(2,5)$.

There are of course other nonsolvable groups of order 120. Two such examples are $\mathrm{Sym}(5)$ and $J \times \mathrm{Alt}(5)$ where $|J| = 2$. Their Sylow 2-subgroups are respectively dihedral and elementary abelian.

14. THE THOMPSON SUBGROUP

Frobenius' theorem (Theorem 13.3) requires that we look at all p-subgroups of G to check whether G has a normal p-complement. In this section we prove a theorem of Thompson which reduces the consideration to two subgroups.

Let P be a p-group. If A is an abelian subgroup of P, let $m(A)$ be the minimum number of generators of A. Set $d(P)$ equal to the maximum of $m(A)$ over all abelian subgroups A of P. We let $\mathcal{J}(P)$, the Thompson subgroup of P, equal the subgroup of P generated by all abelian subgroups A with $m(A) = d(P)$. Clearly $\mathcal{J}(P)$ is characteristic in P. In fact if $P \supseteq P_1 \supseteq \mathcal{J}(P)$ then certainly $\mathcal{J}(P) = \mathcal{J}(P_1)$ so $\mathcal{J}(P)$ is characteristic in P_1.

The two subgroups of interest are the center and the Thompson subgroup of a Sylow p-subgroup of G.

We first discuss a few facts concerning the action of a group on an abelian group V. For convenience we will use additive notation for V in the next five results. We say G acts irreducibly on V if there is is no proper G-invariant subgroup of V. We say G acts nontrivially on V if some element of G does not act like the identity. Let α denote the map $G \rightarrow \text{Aut } V$ so that if $g \in G$ then $\alpha(g) \in \text{Aut } V$. Let $\sigma(G)$ denote the endomorphism $\sigma(G) = \sum_{g \in G} \alpha(g)$.

PROPOSITION 14.1. Let G act on abelian group V and suppose that $|G|$ and $|V|$ are relatively prime. Then $V = V_1 + V_2$ is a direct sum of G-invariant subgroups of V with $V_1 = \mathcal{L}_V(G)$. If further H acts on V and $G \Delta H$ then the V_i are H-invariant.

Proof. Set $\sigma = \sigma(G)$. Let V_1 be the kernel of σ and let V_2 be the image of σ. Clearly V_1 and V_2 are G-invariant subgroups of V and $|V_1||V_2| = |V|$. Let $Z = \mathcal{L}_V(G)$ so that Z is also G-invariant. Clearly $Z \supseteq V_2$. We show that $Z \cap V_1 = \langle 0 \rangle$ and this will clearly yield the result. Let $v \in Z \cap V_1$. Since $v \in Z$, $v\sigma = v\,|G|$ and since $v \in V_1$, $v\sigma = 0$. Hence $v\,|G| = 0$. Since $|G|$ is prime to $|V|$, this yields $v = 0$. If now $G \Delta H$ then σ clearly commutes with the action of H on V so the result follows.

COROLLARY 14.2. Let G act nontrivially on abelian group V and suppose that $|G|$ and $|V|$ are relatively prime. Then there exists a G-invariant subgroup W of V on which G acts nontrivially and irreducibly.

Proof. Let V_1 and V_2 be as in the previous result. By assumption $V_2 \neq \langle 0 \rangle$. Let $W \neq \langle 0 \rangle$ be a minimal G-invariant subgroup of V_2. Clearly G acts irreducibly on W. Since $W \cap \mathcal{L}_V(G) = \langle 0 \rangle$ we see that G acts nontrivially.

COROLLARY 14.3. Let G be a p'-group acting nontrivially on an abelian p-group V. Then G acts nontrivially on the subgroup V_0 of V with $V_0 = \{v \in V \mid vp = 0\}$.

PROPOSITION 14.4. Let G be the disjoint union of the $t+1$ subgroups $H_0, H_1, \ldots, H_t$. Suppose G acts on abelian group V. Then either $Vt = \langle 0 \rangle$ or for some i we have $\mathcal{L}_V(H_i) \neq \langle 0 \rangle$.

Proof. Say $\sigma(H_i) \neq 0$ for some i. If $v \in V$ is chose with $v\sigma(H_i) \neq 0$ then clearly $v\sigma(H_i) \in \mathcal{L}_V(H_i)$. Thus we can assume that for all i, $\sigma(H_i) = 0$. For the same reason we can assume that $\sigma(G) = 0$. From the fact that $G^{\#} = \bigcup H_i^{\#}$ is a disjoint union we have $t = (\sum \sigma(H_i)) - \sigma(G) = 0$ and hence $Vt = \langle 0 \rangle$.

COROLLARY 14.5. Let G act faithfully and irreducibly on abelian group V. Suppose that $|G|$ and $|V|$ are relatively prime. Then $\mathfrak{Z}(G)$ is cyclic.

<u>Proof</u>. If $\mathfrak{Z}(G)$ is not cyclic then G has a central subgroup H which is abelian of type (p, p). Then H is the disjoint union of $p+1$ subgroups $J_0, J_1, \ldots, J_p$ of order p. Since $p \nmid |V|$, $Vp \neq \langle 0 \rangle$ and hence by Proposition 14.4, $\mathcal{L}_V(J_i) \neq \langle 0 \rangle$ for some i. Now G acts faithfully so $\mathcal{L}_V(J_i) \neq V$. Finally since $J_i \triangleleft G$, $\mathcal{L}_V(J_i)$ is a proper G-invariant subgroup of V and G does not act irreducibly, a contradiction.

We now turn to the main result of this section.

THEOREM 14.6. (Thompson) Let p be an odd prime and let G_p be a Sylow p-subgroup of G. Suppose that both

$\mathcal{L}_G(\mathfrak{Z}(G_p))$ and $\mathcal{N}_G(\mathcal{J}(G_p))$ have normal p-complements. Then G has a normal p-complement.

Proof. Suppose false and let G be a counterexample of minimal order. Note that since all Sylow p-subgroups of G are conjugate, the assumption holds for all such G_p.

Step 1. Thompson ordering.

Let $\underline{H}$ be the set of p-subgroups H of G such that $\mathcal{N}_G(H)$ does not have a normal p-complement. By Proposition 13.2 and Theorem 13.3, $\underline{H}$ is nonempty. If $L \subseteq G$, let $|L|_p$ denote the p-part of the order of L. If $H, K \in \underline{H}$ we say that $H \leq\leq K$ if and only if one of the following holds.

a. $|\mathcal{N}_G(H)|_p < |\mathcal{N}_G(K)|_p$

b. $|\mathcal{N}_G(H)|_p = |\mathcal{N}_G(K)|_p$ and $|H| < |K|$

c. $H = K$.

Choose $H \in \underline{H}$ maximal in this ordering. Set $N = \mathcal{N}_G(H)$. We fix this throughout the rest of this proof. Also let P be a fixed Sylow p-subgroup of N and let G_p

be one for G with $G_p \supseteq P \supseteq H$.

<u>Step 2</u>. $H \neq G_p$.

If $H = G_p$ then $N \subseteq \mathfrak{N}_G(\mathfrak{J}(G_p))$ and the latter group has a normal p-complement. Hence N has a normal p-complement, a contradiction.

<u>Step 3</u>. $\bar{N} = N/H$ has a normal p-complement.

Now P is a Sylow p-subgroup of N. Since $H \neq G_p$ if follows that $\mathfrak{N}_{G_p}(H) > H$ and hence $P > H$. Let $\bar{P}$ be the image of P in $\bar{N}$ so that $\bar{P}$ is a Sylow p-subgroup of $\bar{N}$.

Suppose $\bar{N}$ does not have a normal p-complement. Then since $|\bar{N}| < |G|$ either $\mathcal{L}_{\bar{N}}(\mathfrak{Z}(\bar{P}))$ or $\mathfrak{N}_{\bar{N}}(\mathfrak{J}(\bar{P}))$ does not have a normal p-complement. Let K be the inverse image in N of either $\mathfrak{Z}(\bar{P})$ or $\mathfrak{J}(\bar{P})$ whichever one fails. Then K is a p-subgroup of G and $\mathfrak{N}_G(K)$ has no normal p-complement.

Since $P \subseteq \mathfrak{N}_G(K)$ we have either $|\mathfrak{N}_G(K)|_p > |\mathfrak{N}_G(H)|_p$ or $|\mathfrak{N}_G(K)|_p = |\mathfrak{N}_G(H)|_p$ and $|K| > |H|$. Hence $K \in \underline{H}$ and $K \trianglerighteq\trianglerighteq H$ but $K \neq H$. This is a contradiction since H is maximal in $\underline{H}$.

Step 4. $N = G$.

We show first that N satisfies the hypothesis of the theorem. Since $G_p \supseteq P \geq H$ we have $\mathfrak{Z}(G_p) \subseteq \mathfrak{N}_G(H) = N$. Now $P\mathfrak{Z}(G_p) \subseteq N \cap G_p$ so $P\mathfrak{Z}(G_p) = P$ and $\mathfrak{Z}(G_p) \subseteq P$. Thus $\mathfrak{Z}(P) \supseteq \mathfrak{Z}(G_p)$ and $\mathfrak{L}_N(\mathfrak{Z}(P)) \subseteq \mathfrak{L}_G(\mathfrak{Z}(P)) \subseteq \mathfrak{L}_G(\mathfrak{Z}(G_p))$. Since $\mathfrak{L}_G(\mathfrak{Z}(G_p))$ has a normal p-complement, the same is true of $\mathfrak{L}_N(\mathfrak{Z}(P))$.

If $P = G_p$ then certainly $\mathfrak{N}_N(\mathfrak{J}(P)) \subseteq \mathfrak{N}_G(\mathfrak{J}(G_p))$ has a normal p-complement. Now suppose $P < G_p$ so that $\mathfrak{N}_{G_p}(P) > P$. Since $\mathfrak{J}(P)$ is characteristic in P this implies that $\mathfrak{N}_G(\mathfrak{J}(P)) \geq \mathfrak{N}_G(P)$ so we have $|\mathfrak{N}_G(\mathfrak{J}(P))|_p > |N|_p = |\mathfrak{N}_G(H)|_p$. By the maximality of H in $\underline{H}$, $\mathfrak{J}(P) \notin \underline{H}$ and hence $\mathfrak{N}_G(\mathfrak{J}(P))$ has a normal p-complement. The same is therefore true of $\mathfrak{N}_N(\mathfrak{J}(P))$.

If $N \neq G$ then by the minimal nature of G, N has a normal p-complement, a contradiction. Thus $N = G$.

Step 5. $O_{p'}(G) = \langle 1 \rangle$.

Let $L = O_{p'}(G)$. We show that $\tilde{G} = G/L$ satisfies the assumptions of the theorem. Let $K \subseteq G_p$. We show that $\widetilde{\mathfrak{N}_G(K)} = \mathfrak{N}_{\tilde{G}}(\tilde{K})$. We have of course $\widetilde{\mathfrak{N}_G(K)} \subseteq \mathfrak{N}_{\tilde{G}}(\tilde{K})$. Conversely let $\tilde{x} \in \mathfrak{N}_{\tilde{G}}(\tilde{K})$. Then $x \in \mathfrak{N}_G(KL)$. Since $L \triangle KL$, K is a Sylow p-subgroup of KL and so there exists $a \in K$, $b \in L$ with $K^x = K^{ab} = K^b$ by Sylow's theorem. Hence $xb^{-1} \in \mathfrak{N}_G(K)$. Since $\widetilde{xb^{-1}} = \tilde{x}$, this fact follows.

We see that $\widetilde{\mathfrak{J}(G_p)} = \mathfrak{J}(\tilde{G}_p)$ so by the above $\widetilde{\mathfrak{N}_G(\mathfrak{J}(G_p))} = \mathfrak{N}_{\tilde{G}}(\mathfrak{J}(\tilde{G}_p))$. Hence the latter group has a normal p-complement.

For K above we show that $\widetilde{\mathfrak{C}_G(K)} = \mathfrak{C}_{\tilde{G}}(\tilde{K})$. We have trivially $\widetilde{\mathfrak{C}_G(K)} \subseteq \mathfrak{C}_{\tilde{G}}(\tilde{K})$. Let $\tilde{x} \in \mathfrak{C}_{\tilde{G}}(\tilde{K}) \subseteq \mathfrak{N}_{\tilde{G}}(\tilde{K})$ so we can assume that $x \in \mathfrak{N}_G(K)$. Hence $(x, K) \subseteq K$. Also $(x, K) \subseteq L$ since $\tilde{x}$ centralizes $\tilde{K}$ and thus $(x, K) \subseteq K \cap L = \langle 1 \rangle$. This says that $x \in \mathfrak{C}_G(K)$ so this fact follows.

We see that $\widetilde{\mathfrak{Z}(G_p)} = \mathfrak{Z}(\tilde{G}_p)$ so by the above $\widetilde{\mathfrak{C}_G(\mathfrak{Z}(G_p))} = \mathfrak{C}_{\tilde{G}}(\mathfrak{Z}(\tilde{G}_p))$ and hence the latter group has a normal p-complement.

If $|L| > 1$, then $|\tilde{G}| < |G|$ so $\tilde{G}$ has a normal p-complement. The complete inverse image in G of this group is then a normal p-complement of G, a contradiction.

<u>Step 6</u>. $H = O_p(G)$ and G is p-solvable of p-length at most 2.

Set $K = O_p(G)$ so that $K \supseteq H$. Since $G = \mathfrak{N}_G(K)$ has no normal p-complement, $K \in \underline{H}$. By the maximality of H and the fact that $G = \mathfrak{N}_G(H) = \mathfrak{N}_G(K)$ we have $H = K$.

By Steps 3 and 4, G/H has a normal p-complement so G is p-solvable of p-length at most 2.

<u>Step 7</u>. $\bar{G} = G/H = \bar{G}_p\bar{M}$ where $\bar{M}$ is a normal p-complement. Also $\bar{M}$ contains no proper $\bar{G}_p$ -invariant subgroup.

Let $\bar{M} > \bar{M}_0 > \langle 1 \rangle$ and suppose that $\bar{M}_0$ is $\bar{G}_p$-invariant. Let M_0 be the complete inverse image of $\bar{M}_0$ in G. Set $G_0 = G_pM_0$. Then $G_0 < G$ since $\bar{G}_0 = \bar{G}_p\bar{M}_0 < \bar{G}$. Since $\mathfrak{L}_{G_0}(\mathfrak{Z}(G_p))$ and $\mathfrak{N}_{G_0}(\mathfrak{J}(G_p))$ have normal p-complements so does G_0. Hence $G_0 = G_pK_0$ with $K_0 \Delta G_0$ and $G_p \cap K_0 = \langle 1 \rangle$. Now $(H, K_0) \subseteq K_0$ since $K_0 \Delta G_0$ and $(H, K_0) \subseteq H$ since $H \Delta G$. Then $(H, K_0) = \langle 1 \rangle$ and $K_0 \neq \langle 1 \rangle$ centralizes H. This is a contradiction by Step 5, Step 6 and Proposition 13.1.

Step 8. $\bar{M} = \bar{Q}$ is an elementary abelian q-group for some prime $q \neq p$ and $\bar{G}_p$ acts irreducibly on $\bar{Q}$. Thus G_p is a maximal subgroup of G.

Let $q \mid |\bar{M}|$ for some prime q. Then $\bar{G}_p$ permutes the Sylow q-subgroups of $\bar{M}$. Since their number divides $|\bar{M}|$, it follows that some orbit has size 1. Hence if $\bar{Q}$ is the fixed Sylow q-subgroup then $\bar{Q}$ is a $\bar{G}_p$-invariant subgroup. By Step 7, $\bar{Q} = \bar{M}$. Clearly $\bar{Q}$ has no proper characteristic subgroups so $\bar{Q}$ is elementary abelian. Moreover $\bar{Q}$ has no proper $\bar{G}_p$-invariant subgroups so $\bar{G}_p$ acts irreducibly.

If $G > L > G_p$ then $\langle 1 \rangle < \bar{L} \cap \bar{Q} < \bar{Q}$ and $\bar{L} \cap \bar{Q}$ is a proper $\bar{G}_p$-invariant subgroup of $\bar{Q}$, a contradiction.

Step 9. There exists an abelian subgroup A of G_p with $m(A) = d(G_p)$ and $A \nsubseteq H$. Let A be a fixed such group of minimal order. If $A_0 = A \cap H$, then A/A_0 is elementary abelian.

If $\mathfrak{J}(G_p) \subseteq H$, then $\mathfrak{J}(G_p)$ being characteristic in H would be normal in G. Hence $G = \mathfrak{N}(\mathfrak{J}(G_p))$ has a normal p-complement, a contradiction. Therefore $\mathfrak{J}(G_p) \nsubseteq H$. Since

$\mathcal{J}(G_p)$ is generated by all abelian groups A with $A \subseteq G_p$ and $m(A) = d(G_p)$ it follows that for at least one such A, $A \nsubseteq H$. Let A be a fixed such group of minimal order and set $A_0 = A \cap H$. Let A_1/A_0 be the subgroup of A/A_0 generated by all elements of order p. Then A_1 is abelian and $A_1 \nsubseteq H$. Since every element of A of order p is contained in A_1 we have $m(A) = m(A_1)$. By the minimality of $|A|$, $A = A_1$ and A/A_0 is elementary abelian.

Step 10. Let $\bar{A} = AH/H$. Then $\bar{G} = \bar{A}\bar{Q}$ and $|\bar{A}| = p$.

We show first that $\bar{G} = \bar{A}\bar{Q}$. We have $\bar{G} = \bar{G}_p\bar{Q}$ and $\bar{G}_p$ normalizes $\bar{Q}$. This action is faithful since $H = O_p(G)$ and the kernel would be a normal p-subgroup of $\bar{G}$. Note that $\bar{A} = AH/H \cong A/A_0 \neq \langle 1 \rangle$.

Now $\bar{A}$ acts nontrivially on $\bar{Q}$. By Corollary 14.2 we can find $\bar{Q}_1 \subseteq \bar{Q}$ on which $\bar{A}$ acts nontrivially and irreducibly. Let G_1 be the complete inverse image in G of $\bar{A}\bar{Q}_1$. Let P_1 be a Sylow p-subgroup of G_1 with $P_1 \supseteq A$. Let G_p be a Sylow p-subgroup of G with $G_p \supseteq P_1$.

Since $H \subseteq P_1$ and $\mathcal{C}_G(H) \subseteq H$ by Proposition 13.1 it follows that $\mathcal{Z}(G_p) \subseteq \mathcal{C}_G(H) \subseteq H \subseteq P_1$ and so $\mathcal{Z}(G_p) \subseteq \mathcal{Z}(P_1)$.

Thus $\mathcal{C}_G(\mathfrak{Z}(G_p)) \supseteq \mathcal{C}_{G_1}(\mathfrak{Z}(P_1))$ and therefore the latter group has a normal p-complement.

Since $A \subseteq P_1$ and $m(A) = d(G_p)$ we have $d(P_1) = d(G_p)$. Thus $A \subseteq \mathfrak{J}(P_1)$. Let Q_2 be a Sylow q-subgroup of $\mathfrak{N}_{G_1}(\mathfrak{J}(P_1))$. Then $(A, Q_2) \subseteq (\mathfrak{J}(P_1), Q_2) \subseteq \mathfrak{J}(P_1)$ and hence $(\bar{A}, \bar{Q}_2)$ is a p-group. Since $\bar{Q}_2 \subseteq \bar{Q}_1$ we have $(\bar{A}, \bar{Q}_2) \subseteq \bar{Q}_1$ is a q-group and hence $(\bar{A}, \bar{Q}_2) = \langle 1 \rangle$. Thus $\bar{Q}_2$ is an $\bar{A}$-invariant subgroup of $\bar{Q}_1$ centralized by $\bar{A}$. This implies that $\bar{Q}_2 = \langle 1 \rangle$ and hence $Q_2 = \langle 1 \rangle$. Thus $\mathfrak{N}_{G_1}(\mathfrak{J}(P_1))$ is a p-group and hence has a normal p-complemen

If $G_1 < G$, then G_1 has a normal p-complement and this group would centralize H, a contradiction. Thus $G = G_1$ and $\bar{G} = \bar{A}\bar{Q}$. By Step 8, $\bar{A}$ acts faithfully and irreducibly on $\bar{Q}$. Hence since $\bar{A}$ is elementary abelian, it is cyclic by Corollary 14.5. This yields $|\bar{A}| = p$.

<u>Step 11</u>. Set $W = \mathfrak{Z}(H)$ and let Z be the subgroup of W generated by all elements of order p. If Q is a Sylow q-subgroup of G then Q normalizes but does not centralize Z.

We have $\mathfrak{Z}(G_p) \subseteq \mathcal{C}_G(H) \subseteq H$ so that $\mathfrak{Z}(G_p) \subseteq W$.

If Q centralizes W then it centralizes $\mathfrak{Z}(G_p)$ and so $\mathfrak{Z}(G_p)$ would be central in G. Since $\mathcal{C}_G(\mathfrak{Z}(G_p))$ has a normal p-complement, this is a contradiction. Thus Q acts nontrivially on W. By Corollary 14.3, Q acts nontrivially on Z.

Step 12. Contradiction.

Since $Z \trianglelefteq G$, G acts on Z by conjugation. The kernel of this action is $\mathcal{C}_G(Z) \geq H$ and hence $\bar{G}$ acts on Z. Since $\bar{Q}$ is the unique minimal normal subgroup of $\bar{G}$ and $\bar{Q}$ acts nontrivially on Z by Step 11 we see that $\bar{G}$ acts faithfully on Z.

By Proposition 14.1 we can write $Z = C + V$ where $C = \mathcal{C}_Z(\bar{Q})$ and V is $\bar{Q}$-invariant. Moreover since $\bar{Q} \trianglelefteq \bar{G}$ we see that V is $\bar{G}$-invariant. As above $\bar{G}$ acts faithfully on V.

Let $d = d(G_p)$. Since $|\bar{A}| = p$ we have $m(A_0) \geq d-1$. Set $V_0 = V \cap A$ and let $m(V_0) = t$, $m(V/V_0) = r$. Now $V \subseteq \mathfrak{Z}(H)$ and so $\langle V, A_0 \rangle$ is abelian. Since V is elementary abelian we have

$$d \geq m(\langle V, A_0\rangle) = m(V) + m(A_0) - m(V \cap A_0)$$
$$= t + r + m(A_0) - t \geq d - 1 + r$$

and $r = 0$ or 1. Hence either $V_0 = V$ or V_0 is maximal in V.

Choose $a \in A - A_0$, $\bar{b} \in \bar{Q}^{\#}$ such that $\bar{a}$ does not centralize $\bar{b}$. Clearly $\bar{a}$ centralizes V_0 and $\bar{a}^{\bar{b}}$ centralizes $V_0{}^{\bar{b}}$. Thus $\langle \bar{a}, \bar{a}^{\bar{b}}\rangle$ centralizes $V_0 \cap V_0{}^{\bar{b}}$ and $[V : V_0 \cap V_0{}^{\bar{b}}] \leq p^2$. Since $\bar{A} = \langle \bar{a}\rangle$ is maximal in $\bar{G}$ and $\bar{a}^{\bar{b}} \notin \bar{A}$ it follows that $\bar{G}$ centralizes $V_0 \cap V_0{}^{\bar{b}}$ and thus by definition of V, $V_0 \cap V_0{}^{\bar{b}} = \langle 1\rangle$ and hence $|V| \leq p^2$. Since $\bar{G}$ is nonabelian and acts faithfully on V we have $|V| = p^2$.

This yields $\bar{G} \subseteq GL(2, p)$ and since $\bar{G}$ is generated by two elements of order p, $\bar{G} \subseteq SL(2, p)$. Thus in $SL(2, p)$ we have an abelian p'-group $\bar{Q}$ which is normalized but not centralized by $\bar{A} \subseteq SL(2, p)$, a group of order p. This is a contradiction by Proposition 13.5 (iii) for $p \neq 2$. This completes the proof of the theorem.

Consider $G = Sym(4)$. This group has no normal 2-complement and the Sylow 2-subgroup G_2 is maximal.

Since $\mathfrak{Z}(G) = \langle 1 \rangle$ it follows that $\mathcal{C}_G(\mathfrak{Z}(G_2)) = G_2$ has a normal 2-complement. Now G_2 is dihedral of order 8 so $\mathfrak{J}(G_2) = G_2$ and $\mathcal{N}_G(\mathfrak{J}(G_2)) = G_2$ has a normal 2-complement. Hence the above result is false for $p = 2$.

We now obtain some applications.

PROPOSITION 14.7. Let G be a primitive permutation group. If G_a is nilpotent but not a 2-group, then G has a regular normal elementary abelian subgroup N.

Proof. If $K \triangle G$ and $K \subseteq G_a$ then K fixes all points and hence $K = \langle 1 \rangle$. If $K \triangle G_a$, then since G_a is maximal we have $\mathcal{N}_G(K) = G_a$ if $K \neq \langle 1 \rangle$. There are two cases to consider.

Suppose first that $H = G_a$ has at least two prime factors. Let P be a Sylow p-subgroup of H. Since $\mathcal{N}_G(P) = H$ it follows that P is a Sylow p-subgroup of G and hence H is a Hall subgroup of G. Let $x, y \in P$ be conjugate in G, say $y = x^z$. Let Q be a Sylow q-subgroup of H with $q \neq p$. Then $x, y \in \mathcal{C}_G(Q)$ and $y \in \mathcal{C}_G(Q), \mathcal{C}_G(Q^z)$

and thus Q and Q^z are Sylow q-subgroups of $\mathcal{L}_G(y)$. Thus there exists $u \in \mathcal{L}_G(y)$ with $Q = Q^{zu}$. Hence $h = zu \in \mathcal{N}_G(Q) = H$ and $x^h = y^u = y$. Let $h = h_1 h_2$ with $h_1 \in P$ and $h_2 \in \mathcal{L}_H(P)$. This is possible since H is nilpotent. Then $x^h = x^{h_1} = y$ and so any two elements of P conjugate in G are conjugate in P.

Let $H = \prod P_i$ and suppose that $x, y \in H$ are conjugate in G. Say $x = \prod x_i$ and $y = \prod y_i$ with $y = x^z$. From the nature of H we have $y_i = x_i^{\,z}$ and hence by the above there exists $h_i \in P_i$ with $y_i = x_i^{\,h_i}$. Set $h = \prod h_i$. Then clearly $y = x^h$. By Corollary 12.5, H has a normal complement N.

Now let $H = G_a$ be a p-group. By assumption $p \neq 2$. If $K = \mathfrak{Z}(H)$ or $\mathfrak{J}(H)$ then $K \Delta H$ so $\mathcal{N}_G(K) = H$ has a normal p-complement. By Theorem 14.6, G has a normal p-complement N.

Clearly N acts semiregularly since $N \cap G_a = \langle 1 \rangle$. Also $G_a < G$ so $N \neq \langle 1 \rangle$ and since G is primitive, N is transitive. This implies that N is regular. Finally by Corollary 10.7, N is an elementary abelian group.

COROLLARY 14.8. (Thompson) Let H be a maximal subgroup of G and suppose that H is nilpotent of odd order. Then G is solvable.

Proof. By induction on $|G|$. Suppose first that we can find K with $\langle 1\rangle < K \subsetneq H$ and $K \triangle G$. Then H/K is a maximal subgroup of G/K so by induction G/K is solvable. Since K is nilpotent the result follows in this case.

Now suppose no such K exists. G permutes the right cosets of H by right multiplication. If a denotes the coset H, then $G_a = H$. Let K be the subgroup of G fixing all points. Then $K \subseteq G_a = H$ and $K \triangle G$ so by assumption $K = \langle 1\rangle$. Hence G is a permutation group on this set and since G_a is maximal, G is primitive. The result follows from Proposition 14.7.

The following fact about a concrete group shows that the above result is false for the prime 2.

PROPOSITION 14.9. The Sylow 2-subgroups of the nonabelian simple group $PSL(2, 17)$ are maximal.

Proof. We prove this instead for the group $SL(2,17)$. It is clear that the two results are equivalent. Let Q be a Sylow 2-subgroup of $G = SL(2,17)$ and suppose by way of contradiction that there exists a subgroup M with $Q < M < G$. We have $|G| = 2^5\, 3^2\, 17$ and Q is quaternion of order 2^5.

Suppose first that $17 \mid |M|$ and let R be a Sylow 17-subgroup of M. As we saw in the proof of Proposition 13.5, $|\eta_G(R)| = 17 \cdot 16$ and hence R is not normal in M. Thus M contains two subgroups of order 17 and by Proposition 13.5 (ii) $M = G$, a contradiction.

Thus we must have $3 \mid |M|$ and $|M| = 2^5\, 3$ or $2^5\, 3^2$. Let T be a Sylow 3-subgroup of G so that $|T| = 9$. Since $y = \begin{bmatrix} 6 & 2 \\ -2 & 8 \end{bmatrix} \in G$ has order 9, it follows that T is cyclic. This implies that all subgroups of G of order 3 are conjugate. Let $x = \begin{bmatrix} -1 & 1 \\ -1 & 0 \end{bmatrix}$ be an element of G of order 3. It is easy to see that the 2×2 matrices which commute with x are all of the form $\begin{bmatrix} a & b \\ -b & a+b \end{bmatrix}$ and hence if $H = GL(2,17)$ then $|\mathcal{L}_H(x)| \leq 17^2 - 1$. Under the determinant map $\begin{bmatrix} 1 & 1 \\ -1 & 2 \end{bmatrix} \in \mathcal{L}_H(x)$ maps onto 3, a generator of the multiplicative group of GF(17) and thus we have $|\mathcal{L}_G(x)| \leq (17^2-1)/(17-1) = 18$. Since $\mathcal{L}_G(x)$ contains the direct product of $Z = \mathfrak{Z}(G)$ and a Sylow 3-subgroup T of G, we have $\mathcal{L}_G(x) = Z \times T$.

Let P be a Sylow 3-subgroup of M and let P^* be the subgroup of P of order 3. If $N = \mathfrak{N}_M(P)$, then since N normalizes P^*, $|\mathrm{Aut}\, P^*| = 2$ and $N \geq Z$ we have by the above $[N:P] = 2$ or 4 and hence $[M:N] = 16$ or 8. By Sylow's theorem $[M:N] \equiv 1 \bmod 3$ and hence $[M:N] = 16$, $[N:P] = 2$ and $N = PZ$. Thus P is in the center of its normalizer in M and so by Theorem 12.7, $Q \triangle M$. Now Aut Q is a 2-group so since P normalizes Q it centralizes Q and $M = Q \times P$. This contradicts $M \neq N$ and the result follows.

15. GROUP REPRESENTATIONS

In this and the following section we develop certain basic aspects of representation theory.

Let F_0 be a prime field, that is F_0 is the field of rational numbers or $F_0 = GF(p)$ for some prime p, and let $\bar{F}_0$ be its algebraic closure. All fields F are assumed to satisfy $F_0 \subseteq F \subseteq \bar{F}_0$ so that $\bar{F} = \bar{F}_0$. If char F denotes the characteristic of F, then a statement of the form char $F \nmid n$ is considered always true if char $F = 0$.

An F-representation of G is a homomorphism A of G into the $n \times n$ nonsingular matrices over F for some integer n. Here n is called the degree of A. Note that this definition implies that $A(1) = I$, the identity matrix.

We say A is faithful if it is faithful as a homomorphism. Two F-representations A and B are similar, written $A \sim B$, if there exists a nonsingular matrix S over F with $A(g) = S^{-1}B(g)S$ for all $g \in G$. This is clearly an equivalence relation.

Let A be an F-representation of G of degree n. We let V be the set of $1 \times n$ row vectors over F and we define the action of G on V by $vg = vA(g)$ for all $v \in V$, $g \in G$. V is called the G-module associated with A. Conversely let V be a vector space over F of dimension n and suppose that G acts on V. If we choose a basis for

V then we obtain an F-representation of G in the obvious way. Moreover different bases give rise to similar representations. Note that the action of G on V is assumed unital so that $v1 = v$ for all $v \in V$.

We consider some examples and definitions.

i. The unit F-representation A of G is of degree 1 and is defined by $A(g) = [1]$ for all $g \in G$.

ii. Suppose G permutes the set $\{v_1, v_2, \ldots, v_n\}$ though not necessarily faithfully. Let V be a vector space over F with basis $v_1, v_2, \ldots, v_n$. Then G acts in the obvious manner on V and with respect to this basis we obtain an F-representation A of G. If $A(g) = [a_{ij}(g)]$ then we see that $a_{ij}(g) = 1$ if $v_i g = v_j$ and 0 otherwise. This is called a permutation F-representation.

iii. Now G permutes its elements by right multiplication. The permutation F-representation obtained from this is called the regular F-representation of G. It is faithful and has degree $|G|$.

iv. Let A and B be two F-representations. We define $A + B$ to be the representation given by

$$(A \dotplus B)(g) = \begin{bmatrix} A(g) & 0 \\ 0 & B(g) \end{bmatrix}.$$

Suppose A has degree n and V is its associated module with natural basis $v_1, v_2, \ldots, v_n$. Similarly let B have degree m with module W and basis $w_1, w_2, \ldots, w_m$. Thus we see that $A \dotplus B$ is the representation of G on $V \dotplus W$ with basis $v_1, v_2, \ldots, v_n, w_1, w_2, \ldots, w_m$. This shows that $A \dotplus B \sim B \dotplus A$. The operation $\dotplus$ is clearly associative. Furthermore if $A \sim A_1$, $B \sim B_1$ then $A \dotplus B \sim A_1 \dotplus B_1$.

v. Let A, B, V, W be as above. We define $A \times B$ to be the F-representation given by

$$(A \times B)(g) = \begin{bmatrix} a_{11}(g)B(g) & a_{12}(g)B(g) & \ldots & a_{1n}(g)B(g) \\ a_{21}(g)B(g) & a_{22}(g)B(g) & \ldots & a_{2n}(g)B(g) \\ \vdots & \vdots & & \vdots \\ a_{n1}(g)B(g) & a_{n2}(g)B(g) & \ldots & a_{nn}(g)B(g) \end{bmatrix}$$

where $A(g) = [a_{ij}(g)]$. We see easily that $A \times B$ is the representation of G on $V \otimes W$ where the latter space has basis $\{v_i \otimes w_j\}$. The action of G is given by

$$(v_i \otimes w_j)g = (v_i g) \otimes (w_j g) = \sum_{r,s} a_{ir}\, b_{js}\, (v_r \otimes w_s).$$

Here the basis is written in the order $v_1 \otimes w_1, v_1 \otimes w_2, \ldots,$ $v_1 \otimes w_m, v_2 \otimes w_1, v_2 \otimes w_2, \ldots, v_2 \otimes w_m, \ldots\ldots, v_n \otimes w_1, v_n \otimes w_2,$ $\ldots, v_n \otimes w_m$. There is an obvious identification of $V \otimes W$ and $W \otimes V$ and this show easily that $A \times B \sim B \times A$. The operation $\times$ is clearly associative. Furthermore if $A \sim A_1$, $B \sim B_1$ then $A \times B \sim A_1 \times B_1$.

vi. Let $A = [a_{ij}]$ be an F-representation of G. If σ is a field automorphism of $\bar{F}$, then $A^\sigma = [a_{ij}^\sigma]$ is clearly an F^σ-representation of G.

vii. Let F and K be fields with $F_0 \subseteq F \subseteq K \subseteq \bar{F}_0$. If A is an F-representation of G then certainly A can be viewed as a K-representation. We denote this extension by A_K. If $K = \bar{F}$ we use the notation $\bar{A}$. Conversely if $A = [a_{ij}]$ is a K-representation of G and if for all $g \in G$ we have $a_{ij}(g) \in F$ then A can be viewed as an F-representation. In this case we say that A is realizeable over F.

viii. Let A be an F-representation of G. We say that A is reducible if $A(g) \sim \begin{bmatrix} B(g) & 0 \\ C(g) & D(g) \end{bmatrix}$ for all $g \in G$, where as usual 0 denotes a matrix with all zero entries. Moreover we assume here that the matrix 0 does in fact occur nontrivially. If A is not reducible, it is irreducible. Let V be the module of dimension n associated with A. If A is reducible as above then by a change of basis we can assume that A has the form on the right. Let this new basis be $v_1, v_2, \ldots, v_r, v_{r+1}, \ldots, v_n$ where B is an $r \times r$ matrix and $1 \leq r < n$. If $W = \langle v_1, v_2, \ldots, v_r \rangle$ then we see easily that $\langle 0 \rangle < W < V$ and W is a G-invariant subspace of V, a G-submodule of V. Clearly B is an F-representation of G, the restriction of A to W, and D corresponds to the action of G on V/W. Conversely suppose we are given A and V and suppose that V contains a proper G-submodule W. We choose a basis for W and extend this to one of V. It is clear that with respect to this new basis the matrices involved have zero entries in the upper right corner. Hence A is reducible. This shows that A is irreducible if and only if V contains no nontrivial G-submodules.

ix. We say that A is completely reducible if and only if $A \sim A_1 + A_2 + \ldots + A_m$ where each A_i is irreducible. Thus A is completely reducible if and only if we have

$V = V_1 + V_2 + \dots + V_m$ where V is the G-module associated with A and each V_i is an irreducible G-submodule.

THEOREM 15.1. (Maschke) Let G be a group and F a field with char $F \nmid |G|$. Then every F-representation of G is completely reducible.

<u>Proof</u>. It clearly suffices to show that if A is reducible then $A \sim B + D$ where B and D are F-representations of G of degree less than that of A. Thus let us assume that $A(g) = \begin{bmatrix} B(g) & 0 \\ C(g) & D(g) \end{bmatrix}$. From $A(g)\,A(h) = A(gh)$ we obtain $B(g)\,B(h) = B(gh)$, $D(g)\,D(h) = D(gh)$ and $C(g)\,B(h) + D(g)\,C(h) = C(gh)$. Multiply the latter equation on the right by $B(h^{-1}) = B(h^{-1}g^{-1})\,B(g)$ to obtain

$$C(g) + D(g)\,C(h)\,B(h^{-1}) = C(gh)\,B(h^{-1}g^{-1})\,B(g).$$

Summing this over all $h \in G$ and dividing by $|G| \neq 0$ yields $C(g) + D(g)\,M = M\,B(g)$ where $M = |G|^{-1}\sum_{h \in G} C(h)\,B(h^{-1})$. If $S = \begin{bmatrix} I & 0 \\ M & I \end{bmatrix}$ then $S^{-1} = \begin{bmatrix} I & 0 \\ -M & I \end{bmatrix}$ and we have

$S^{-1} A(g) S = \begin{bmatrix} B(g) & 0 \\ 0 & D(g) \end{bmatrix}$. Hence $A \sim B + D$ and the result follows.

Let A and B be two F-representations of G. A matrix X over F is said to intertwine A and B (in that order) if for all $g \in G$ we have $A(g)X = XB(g)$. We denote the set of all such X by $I(A, B)$.

THEOREM 15.2. (Schur's Lemma) Let A and B be two irreducible F-representations of G.

i. If $A \nsim B$, then $I(A, B) = \{0\}$.

ii. $I(A, A)$ is closed under matrix addition and multiplication. It is a division ring containing the set of scalar matrices in its center.

iii. If $F = \bar{F}$, then $I(A, A)$ is the set of scalar matrices.

Proof. Let V and W be the G-modules associated with A and B respectively. Let $X \in I(A, B)$ and suppose that $X \neq 0$. We can view X as a linear transformation from V to W and $X \in I(A, B)$ implies that X commutes with the action of G. Set $W_0 = VX$, the image of V under X. Then W_0 is a subspace of W and for all $g \in G$, $W_0B(g) = VXB(g) = VA(g)X = VX = W_0$ so that W_0 is a G-submodule of W. Since B is irreducible $W_0 = W$ or $\langle 0 \rangle$ and since $X \neq 0$, $W = W_0$. Thus X is onto. Set $V_0 = \{v \in V \mid vX = 0\}$, the kernel of X. Then for all $g \in G$, $V_0A(g)X = V_0XB(g) = \langle 0 \rangle B(g) = \langle 0 \rangle$ so that $V_0A(g) \subseteq V_0$. Hence V_0 is a G-submodule of V. Since A is irreducible, $V_0 = V$ or $\langle 0 \rangle$ and since $X \neq 0$, $V_0 = \langle 0 \rangle$. Thus X is one to one and onto so X^{-1} exists. From $A(g)X = XB(g)$ we obtain $B(g) = X^{-1}A(g)X$ and $B \sim A$. This yields (i).

If $B = A$ then it is trivial to check that $I(A, A)$ is a subring of the $n \times n$ matrices over F where n is the degree of A. Clearly $I(A, A)$ contains the scalar matrices in its center. Finally if $X \in I(A, A)$ and $X \neq 0$ then by the above X^{-1} exists. From $A(g)X = XA(g)$ we obtain by multiplying on the right and left by X^{-1}, $X^{-1}A(g) = A(g)X^{-1}$ and so $X^{-1} \in I(A, A)$. This yields (ii).

Finally let $F = \bar{F}$ so that F is algebraically closed. Then $D = I(A, A)$ is a division ring finite dimensional over the scalar matrices, a field isomorphic to F. Since these scalars are in the center of D, this yields (iii).

If A is an irreducible F-representation it is quite possible that under a field extension A_K is reducible. We say that A is absolutely irreducible if $\bar{A}$ is irreducible. Clearly A must be irreducible if it is absolutely irreducible.

COROLLARY 15.3. If A is an absolutely irreducible F-representation of G then I(A, A) consists entirely of scalar matrices.

Proof. Let $X \in I(A, A)$ and let λ be an eigenvalue of matrix X with $\lambda \in \bar{F}$. Then $X - \lambda I \in I(\bar{A}, \bar{A})$. Clearly $X - \lambda I$ is singular and hence since $\bar{A}$ is irreducible we must have $X - \lambda I = 0$ and $X = \lambda I$. Since $X \in I(A, A)$, $\lambda \in F$ and the result follows.

COROLLARY 15.4. Let A be a faithful irreducible F-representation of G. Then $\mathfrak{Z}(G)$ is cyclic and in particular if G is abelian, then G is cyclic. If A is absolutely irreducible then $A(\mathfrak{Z}(G))$ consists of scalar matrices and in particular if G is abelian, then A has degree 1.

<u>Proof</u>. Let $g \in G$, $z \in \mathfrak{Z}(G)$. Then $A(g)A(z) = A(z)A(g)$ so $A(z) \in I(A, A)$. If A is absolutely irreducible then by the above $A(z)$ is a scalar matrix. If $G = \mathfrak{Z}(G)$ then all $A(g)$ are scalar matrices and since A is irreducible, A has degree 1. In general let D be the smallest division subring of the division ring $I(A, A)$ containing the matrices $A(\mathfrak{Z}(G))$. Since all these matrices commute we see that D is a field and hence $A(\mathfrak{Z}(G))$ is a finite multiplicative subgroup of a field. This implies that $A(\mathfrak{Z}(G))$ is cyclic and since A is faithful, $\mathfrak{Z}(G)$ is cyclic.

Let $\alpha, \beta \in FG$ where FG denotes the set of all functions from G to F. We define an inner product $(\ ,\ )$ on FG by $(\alpha, \beta) = \sum_g \alpha(g^{-1})\beta(g)$. It is clear that $(\ ,\ )$ is linear and symmetric. If A is an F-representation of G with $A(g) = [a_{ij}(g)]$ then certainly $a_{ij} \in FG$.

THEOREM 15.5. (Schur) Let $A = [a_{ij}]$ and $B = [b_{ij}]$ be irreducible F-representations of G.

i. If A and B are not similar then $(a_{is}, b_{tj}) = 0$ for all i, s, t, j.

ii. If A is absolutely irreducible of degree n and if char $F \nmid |G|$ then $(a_{is}, a_{tj}) = \delta_{ij} \delta_{st} |G|/n$.

Proof. Let S be any matrix of suitable size with coefficients in F and set $f(S) = \sum_g A(g^{-1})SB(g)$. Then for all $h \in G$, $A(h)f(S) = f(S)B(h)$ so that $f(S) \in I(A, B)$. Let E_{st} be the matrix with 1 in the (s, t) entry and 0 elsewhere. The (i, j) entry of $f(E_{st})$ is easily seen to be (a_{is}, b_{tj}).

If A and B are not similar then $f(S) = 0$ by Theorem 15.2 and (i) follows.

Now let $A = B$ be absolutely irreducible and assume that char $F \nmid |G|$. By Theorem 15.2, $f(E_{st}) = e_{st} I$. Thus $e_{st} \delta_{ij} = (a_{is}, a_{tj}) = (a_{tj}, a_{is}) = e_{ji} \delta_{ts}$. Thus $e_{st} = 0$ if $s \neq t$ and $e_{ss} = e$ is independent of s. It remains to evaluate e. We have $I = E_{11} + E_{22} + \dots + E_{nn}$ so

$$neI = \sum f(E_{ii}) = \sum_g \sum_i A(g^{-1}) E_{ii} A(g)$$
$$= \sum_g A(g^{-1}) A(g) = |G| I.$$

Since $|G| \neq 0$ in F, $n \neq 0$ and $e = |G|/n$. This completes the proof.

Let A be an F-representation of G and let n(A) be its degree. We define the span of A, Span A, to be the subspace of FG spanned by all the functions a_{ij}. We list some basic properties of the span.

PROPOSITION 15.6. Let A and B be F-representations of G.

i. If $A \sim B$ then Span A = Span B.

ii. Span $(A+B) \subseteq \langle$Span A, Span B$\rangle$.

iii. If $K \supseteq F$ then Span $A_K = K \otimes$ Span A, where the latter is the K vector space spanned by the elements of Span A.

iv. $\dim_F$ Span $A \leq n(A)^2$.

<u>Proof</u>. If $A \sim B$ then $A(g) = S^{-1}B(g)S$ for some nonsingular matrix S. Thus each a_{ij} is an F-linear sum of the functions b_{ij} and Span $A \subseteq$ Span B. Similarly Span $B \subseteq$ Span A and (i) follows. Statements (ii), (iii) and

(iv) are immediate.

PROPOSITION 15.7. Suppose that char $F \nmid |G|$.

i. F-representation A is absolutely irreducible if and only if $\dim_F \text{Span } A = n(A)^2$.

ii. Let A and B be absolutely irreducible. Then the statements (a) $A \sim B$, (b) $(\text{Span } A, \text{Span } B) \neq 0$ and (c) $\bar{A} \sim \bar{B}$ are equivalent.

iii. G has only finitely many pairwise nonsimilar absolutely irreducible F-representations.

iv. Let $A_1, A_2, \ldots, A_k$ be representatives of each of the equivalence classes of irreducible $\bar{F}$-representations. Then $n(A_1)^2 + n(A_2)^2 + \ldots + n(A_k)^2 = |G|$.

Proof. (i) Since $\dim_{\bar{F}} (\bar{F} \otimes \text{Span } A) = \dim_F \text{Span } A$ it suffices to assume that $F = \bar{F}$. If A is reducible then we can assume that $A = B + C$. Thus some a_{ij} is the zero function so clearly $\dim_F \text{Span } A < n(A)^2$. Now let $A = [a_{ij}]$ be irreducible. We show that the functions a_{ij} are linearly independent. Say $\sum x_{ij} a_{ij} = 0$ for $x_{ij} \in F$.

We take the inner product of this expression with a_{rs} and obtain by Theorem 15.5 $x_{sr}|G|/n(A) = 0$. Since char $F \nmid |G|$ this yields $x_{sr} = 0$. Thus $\dim_F \text{Span } A = n(A)^2$.

(ii) Let A and B be absolutely irreducible F-representations. By Theorem 15.5 we see that $A \sim B$ if and only if Span A and Span B are orthogonal. Similarly $\bar{A} \sim \bar{B}$ if and only if Span $\bar{A}$ and Span $\bar{B}$ are orthogonal. Since Span $\bar{A} = \bar{F} \otimes$ Span A and Span $\bar{B} = \bar{F} \otimes$ Span B we see that (ii) follows.

(iii) Let $A_1, \ldots, A_m$ be pairwise nonsimilar absolutely irreducible F-representations. Then Span A_i and Span A_j are orthogonal for $i \neq j$. As in the proof of (i) we see that the associated functions of the A_i's are all linearly independent. Thus $FG \supseteq \text{Span } A_1 + \ldots + \text{Span } A_m$ where the latter is a direct sum. By considering dimensions we have $|G| \geq n(A_1)^2 + \ldots + n(A_m)^2$ and thus (iii) clearly follows.

(iv) Let $A_1, \ldots, A_k$ be the given representatives. By the above we have $|G| \geq n(A_1)^2 + n(A_2)^2 + \ldots + n(A_k)^2$. Let R be the regular $\bar{F}$-representation of G. By Theorem 15.1 $R \sim a_1A_1 + a_2A_2 + \ldots + a_kA_k$ where the integers a_i denote the multiplicity. Thus $\text{Span } R \subseteq \langle \text{Span } A_1, \ldots, \text{Span } A_k \rangle$ and $\dim_{\bar{F}} \text{Span } R \leq n(A_1)^2 + \ldots + n(A_k)^2$. Now $R = [r_{gh}]$ is indexed by the elements of G. The functions r_{1g} satisfy $r_{1g}(g) = 1$ and $r_{1g}(h) = 0$ for $h \neq g$. Thus these functions are linearly independent and $|G| \leq \dim_{\bar{F}} \text{Span } R$ This clearly yields the result.

We say F is a splitting field of G if there are absolutely irreducible F-representations $A_1, A_2, \ldots, A_k$ such that ever irreducible $\bar{F}$-representation of G is similar to one of $\bar{A}_1, \bar{A}_2, \ldots, \bar{A}_k$.

PROPOSITION 15.8. Let $\text{char } F_0 \nmid |G|$. Then there exists a splitting field F of G with $(F:F_0) < \infty$.

Proof. Let $B_1, B_2, \ldots, B_k$ be a system of representatives of the equivalence classes of irreducible $\bar{F}$-representations of G. Say $B_r = [b_{ij}^{(r)}]$. Then $\{b_{ij}^{(r)}(g)\}$ is a finite set of numbers algebraic over F_0. Hence there exists a field F with $F_0 \subseteq F \subseteq \bar{F}_0$, $(F:F_0) < \infty$ and $b_{ij}^{(r)}(g) \in F$ for all such elements. Thus each B_i is realizable over F and let A_i be the representation B_i viewed as an F-representation. Since $\bar{A}_i = B_i$, F is a splitting field and the result follows.

Let D be an integral domain with quotient field F. An F-representation A of G is a D-representation if for all $g \in G$ the entries of A(g) lie in D.

PROPOSITION 15.9. Let D be a principal ideal domain with quotient field F. Then every F-representation of G is similar to a D-representation.

Proof. Let A be an F-representation of G and let V be the associated G-module with basis $v_1, v_2, \ldots, v_n$. Let W be the D-module generated by the elements $\{v_i A(g)\}$. Then W is a finitely generated torsion free D-module and so it has a basis $w_1, w_2, \ldots, w_m$. It is easy to see that $\{w_i\}$ is also an F-basis of V so $m = n$. Since W is clearly a G-module we see that with respect to this new basis all the matrices of the representation have entries in D.

Let F be a finite extension of $\mathbb{Q}$, the field of rational numbers. Let p be a prime and let $\mathfrak{P}$ be a prime ideal in the ring of algebraic integers of F such that $p \in \mathfrak{P}$. Define D by $D = \{a/b \mid a, b$ are algebraic integers in F and $b \notin \mathfrak{P}\}$. The elements of D are called local integers at $\mathfrak{P}$. We list certain well known facts.

i. D is a principal ideal domain with quotient field F.

ii. $D\mathfrak{P}$ is the unique maximal ideal of D and $D/D\mathfrak{P}$ is a finite field of characteristic p.

iii. An element of F is an algebraic integer if and only if it is a local integer at $\mathfrak{P}$ for all prime ideals $\mathfrak{P}$.

THEOREM 15.10. The degrees of the irreducible $\bar{\mathbb{Q}}$-representations of G divide $|G|$.

Proof. Let F be a splitting field of G with $\mathbb{Q} \subseteq F \subseteq \bar{\mathbb{Q}}$ and $(F:\mathbb{Q}) < \infty$. Let A be an absolutely irreducible F-representation of G with $n(A) = n$. Let $\mathfrak{P}$ be a prime ideal in the ring of algebraic integers of F and let D be as above. Then by Proposition 15.9 there is a D-representation B of G with $B \sim A$. Say $B = [b_{ij}]$. By Theorem 15.5 $|G|/n = \Sigma\, b_{11}(g^{-1})b_{11}(g) \in D$. Thus $|G|/n$ is a local integer for all primes $\mathfrak{P}$ and hence $|G|/n$ is an algebraic integer. Since $|G|/n$ is rational, it is an integer and $n \mid |G|$. Thus the result is proved.

THEOREM 15.11. Let p be a prime with $p \nmid |G|$. Then there is a one to one correspondence $A_i \leftrightarrow A_i^*$ between $\{A_1, A_2, \ldots, A_k\}$ a set of representatives of the equivalence classes of irreducible $\overline{\mathbb{Q}}$-representations of G and $\{A_1^*, A_2^*, \ldots, A_k^*\}$ a set of representatives of the irreducible $\overline{GF(p)}$-representations. Furthermore the eigenvalues of the matrix $A_i^*(g)$ are equal to the images of the eigenvalues of the matrix $A_i(g)$ under a map Θ. Here Θ is an isomorphism from the multiplicative group of $|G|^{th}$ roots of unity in $\overline{\mathbb{Q}}$ onto the group of $|G|^{th}$ roots of unity in $\overline{GF(p)}$.

Proof. Let F be a splitting field of G with

$(F:Q) < \infty$ and let $\{B_1, B_2, \ldots, B_k\}$ be a set of representatives of the equivalence classes of absolutely irreducible F-representations of G. We can assume that F contains a primitive $|G|^{th}$ root of unity. Set $A_i = \bar{B}_i$ so that $\{A_1, A_2, \ldots, A_k\}$ is a set of representatives of the irreducible $\bar{\mathbb{Q}}$-representations of G.

Let $\mathfrak{P}$ be a prime ideal in the ring of algebraic integers in F with $p \in \mathfrak{P}$ and let D be the ring of local integers at $\mathfrak{P}$. We can assume that each $B_i = [b_{rs}^{(i)}]$ is a D-representation. Let $*$ denote the homomorphism $D \to D/D\mathfrak{P} = F^*$, where F^* is a field of characteristic p. Clearly $B_i^* = [b_{rs}^{(i)*}]$ is an F^*-representation of G. From the Schur relations (Theorem 15.5) for absolutely irreducible B_i and from the fact that $|G|/n(B_i) \neq 0$ in F^* we see easily that the functions $b_{rs}^{(i)*}$ are linearly independent. Hence $\dim_{F^*} \operatorname{Span} B_i^* = n(B_i^*)^2$ and B_i^* is an absolutely irreducible F^*-representation. Since for $i \neq j$, $(\operatorname{Span} B_i, \operatorname{Span} B_j) = 0$ we see that $(\operatorname{Span} B_i^*, \operatorname{Span} B_j^*) = 0$ and hence B_i^* and B_j^* are not similar.

Set $A_i^* = \overline{B_i^*}$ and we let $A_i \leftrightarrow A_i^*$. By the above this is a one to one correspondence between $\{A_i\}$ and $\{A_i^*\}$

where the latter is a set of representatives of some of the equivalence classes of irreducible $\overline{GF(p)}$-representations. Now we have $n(A_i^*) = n(A_i)$ and $\sum n(A_i^*)^2 = \sum n(A_i)^2 = |G|$. This implies that every irreducible $\overline{GF(p)}$-representation is similar to one of the A_i^* and hence the first part of the result is proved.

We use $w(S)$ to denote the characteristic polynomial of matrix S. Then certainly for all i and $g \in G$ we have $w(A_i(g)) = w(B_i(g)) \xrightarrow{*} w(B_i^*(g)) = w(A_i^*(g))$. Let $m = |G|$ so that $g^m = 1$. Then certainly the eigenvalues of $A_i(g)$ are all m^{th} roots of unity. These are contained in F by assumption and thus they are clearly contained in D. If $w(B_i(g)) = \prod(x - \varepsilon_\lambda)$ with $\varepsilon_\lambda \in D$ then certainly we have $w(B_i^*(g)) = \prod(x - \varepsilon_\lambda^*)$. Let L denote the multiplicative group of mth roots of unity in $\overline{\mathbb{Q}}$ so that $L \subseteq D$ and let $\tilde{L}$ denote the corresponding group in $\overline{GF(p)}$. Then $|L| = m$ and $|\tilde{L}| \leq m$. If Θ denotes the restriction of $*$ to L, then Θ is a homomorphism of L into $\tilde{L}$. The result will follow if we show that Θ is an isomorphism. Since $|\tilde{L}| \leq |L|$ it suffices to show that Θ is one to one. If this were not the case then for some $\xi \in L^{\#}$, $\xi^* = 1$.

Since $1+\zeta+\zeta^2+\ldots+\zeta^{m-1}=0$ we have $m=0$ in $\overline{GF(p)}$ and this is a contradiction since $p \nmid |G|$. Thus the result follows.

16. GROUP CHARACTERS

We now restrict our attention to the field $\overline{\mathbb{Q}}$, the algebraic closure of the rational numbers $\mathbb{Q}$. By a representation of G we will mean a $\overline{\mathbb{Q}}$-representation.

Let $A=[a_{ij}]$ be a square matrix. The trace of A, written $\operatorname{tr} A$, is equal to the sum of the elements of A on the main diagonal. Thus $\operatorname{tr} A = a_{11}+a_{22}+\ldots+a_{nn}$.

LEMMA 16.1. Let A and B be $n\times n$ matrices. Then $\operatorname{tr} AB = \operatorname{tr} BA$. Thus if S is a nonsingular matrix then $\operatorname{tr} S^{-1}AS = \operatorname{tr} A$.

Proof. Let $A=[a_{ij}]$ and $B=[b_{ij}]$. Then $\operatorname{tr} AB = \sum_i \sum_j a_{ij}b_{ji}$ and the right hand side is symmetric in A and B. Thus $\operatorname{tr} AB = \operatorname{tr} BA$. Finally we have

$\operatorname{tr} S^{-1}(AS) = \operatorname{tr}(AS)S^{-1} = \operatorname{tr} A$ and the result follows.

Let A be a representation of G. We define the character χ_A of A to be the function $\chi_A(g) = \operatorname{tr} A(g)$. We say χ is a character of G if $\chi = \chi_A$ for some representation A. If A can be chosen to be irreducible, then χ is called an irreducible character of G.

PROPOSITION 16.2. Let A and B be two representations of G.

i. If $A \sim B$ then $\chi_A = \chi_B$.

ii. If g, h are conjugate in G then $\chi_A(g) = \chi_A(h)$.

iii. $\chi_{A+B} = \chi_A + \chi_B$.

iv. $\chi_{A \times B} = \chi_A \chi_B$.

v. If σ is a field automorphism then $\chi_{A^\sigma} = (\chi_A)^\sigma$.

Proof. (i) and (ii) follow from the fact that $\operatorname{tr} S^{-1}AS = \operatorname{tr} A$. (iii) and (iv) are obvious. If $A = [a_{ij}]$, $B = [b_{ij}]$ then we see easily that

$$\begin{aligned}\operatorname{tr} A \times B &= a_{11} \operatorname{tr} B + a_{22} \operatorname{tr} B + \dots + a_{nn} \operatorname{tr} B \\ &= (a_{11} + a_{22} + \dots + a_{nn}) \operatorname{tr} B = (\operatorname{tr} A)(\operatorname{tr} B)\end{aligned}$$

and (iv) follows.

The above result says that the sum and product of two characters is again a character. By a generalized character we mean the difference of two characters. If $I(G)$ denotes the set of all generalized characters, then $I(G)$ is a ring. We let $I_0(G)$ denote the subring of $I(G)$ consisting of all those generalized characters which vanish at the identity, that is $I_0(G) = \{\alpha \in I(G) \mid \alpha(1) = 0\}$.

Part (ii) of Proposition 16.2 states that the characters of G are class functions, that is they are constant on the classes of G. We let $\bar{Z}G$ denote the set of all class functions from G into $\bar{\mathbb{Q}}$. Thus we have $I_0(G) \subseteq I(G) \subseteq \bar{Z}G$.

Throughout this section let ε be a fixed primitive $|G|^{th}$ root of unity. If σ is a field automorphism of $\mathbb{Q}(\varepsilon)$ then for some integer r, $\varepsilon\sigma = \varepsilon^r$. Clearly σ is uniquely determined by r modulo $|G|$ and we denote this automorphism by σ_r. We see easily that $\sigma_r \sigma_s = \sigma_{rs}$. Thus as in the proof of Theorem 9.1 we see that this Galois group is contained isomorphically in J_n^* where $n = |G|$. In fact, since it is known that the Galois group is transitive on the primitive $|G|^{th}$ roots of unity, we see that the group is isomorphic to J_n^*.

PROPOSITION 16.3. Let χ be a character of G and let σ_r be a field automorphism of $\mathbb{Q}(\varepsilon)$ with $\varepsilon\sigma_r = \varepsilon^r$. If $g \in G$, then

i. $\chi(g) \in \mathbb{Q}(\varepsilon)$.

ii. χ^{σ_r} is a character of G.

iii. $\chi^{\sigma_r}(g) = \chi(g^r)$.

Proof. Let $H = \langle g \rangle$ so that H is a cyclic subgroup of G and let $\chi = \chi_A$. Certainly $A|H$, the restriction of A to H, is a representation of H and hence by Theorem 15.1 and Corollary 15.4 there is a nonsingular matrix S with $S^{-1}(A|H)S = B_1 + B_2 + \ldots + B_n$ where the representations B_i of H have degree 1. Set $B = S^{-1}AS$ so that $B \sim A$ and $\chi = \chi_B$. We have $\chi(g) = \chi_{B_1}(g) + \chi_{B_2}(g) + \ldots + \chi_{B_n}(g)$.

Now a representation of degree 1 is essentially a homomorphism into $\overline{\mathbb{Q}}$ and thus into the multiplicative group of $|G|^{th}$ roots of unity in $\overline{\mathbb{Q}}$. This shows that

$\chi_{B_i}(g) \in \mathbb{Q}(\varepsilon)$ and hence $\chi(g) \in \mathbb{Q}(\varepsilon)$. In particular it now makes sense to even speak about χ^{σ_r}.

Let us extend σ_r to an automorphism σ of $\bar{\mathbb{Q}}$. Since $\chi(g) \in \mathbb{Q}(\varepsilon)$ we have $\chi^{\sigma_r} = \chi^{\sigma} = \chi_{B^\sigma}$ and (ii) follows. From $\chi(g) = \chi_{B_1}(g) + \chi_{B_2}(g) + \ldots + \chi_{B_n}(g)$ we see that to prove (iii) it suffices to assume that χ is linear, that is χ has degree 1. In this case $g \to \chi(g)$ is a homomorphism and then $\chi^{\sigma_r}(g) = \chi(g)^r = \chi(g^r)$ and (iii) follows.

Let $\alpha, \beta \in \bar{Z}G$. We define a Hermitian inner product by

$$[\alpha, \beta] = [\alpha, \beta]_G = |G|^{-1} \sum_{g \in G} \alpha(g) \overline{\beta(g)}$$

where $^{-}$ denotes complex conjugation. This is clearly Hermitian symmetric and positive definite.

THEOREM 16.4. (Schur) Let A and B be irreducible representations of G. Then $[\chi_A, \chi_B] = 1$ if A and B are similar and $[\chi_A, \chi_B] = 0$ if A and B are not similar.

<u>Proof</u>. Let $A = [a_{ij}]$ and $B = [b_{ij}]$. By Proposition 16.3 (iii) with $r = -1$ we have $\overline{\chi_B(g)} = \chi_B(g^{-1})$. Then

$$|G|[\chi_A, \chi_B] = \Sigma_g \chi_A(g)\chi_B(g^{-1})$$
$$= \Sigma_i \Sigma_j \Sigma_g a_{ii}(g) b_{jj}(g^{-1}).$$

If A and B are not similar then by Theorem 15.5 we have $[\chi_A, \chi_B] = 0$. If $A \sim B$ then we can assume that $B = A$. If $n = n(A)$ this yields with Theorem 15.5

$$|G|[\chi_A, \chi_B] = \Sigma_i \Sigma_j \Sigma_g a_{ii}(g) b_{jj}(g^{-1})$$
$$= \Sigma_i \Sigma_g a_{ii}(g) b_{ii}(g^{-1}) = n|G|/n$$

and the result follows.

Let $\chi_1, \chi_2, \ldots, \chi_k$ denote the characters of the k equivalence classes of irreducible representations of G. By the above these form an orthonormal subset of $\bar{Z}G$ and hence they are linearly independent. If $\chi \in I(G)$ then by Theorem 15.1 and Proposition 16.2 we have $\chi = a_1\chi_1 + a_2\chi_2 + \ldots + a_k\chi_k$ for suitable integers a_i. We see easily that $a_i = [\chi, \chi_i]$. If $\alpha \in \bar{Z}G$, we set $\|\alpha\|^2 = [\alpha, \alpha]$. Then $\|\chi\|^2 = a_1^2 + a_2^2 + \ldots + a_k^2$.

Let G be a group and let H be a subgroup. If $\alpha \in \bar{Z}G$ then clearly $\alpha|H$, the restriction of α to H, is an element of $\bar{Z}H$. Thus we have a map $\bar{Z}G \rightarrow \bar{Z}H$. In the other direction, let $\alpha \in \bar{Z}H$ and let $\alpha_0 \in \bar{Q}G$ be defined by $\alpha_0(g) = \alpha(g)$ if $g \in H$ and $\alpha_0(g) = 0$ if $g \in G-H$. Set $\alpha^*(g) = |H|^{-1} \sum_{x \in G} \alpha_0(x^{-1}gx)$. Clearly $\alpha^* \in \bar{Z}G$. We call α^* the function induced from α.

THEOREM 16.5. Let H be a subgroup of G.

i. The restriction map sends $\bar{Z}G \rightarrow \bar{Z}H$, $I(G) \rightarrow I(H)$ and $I_0(G) \rightarrow I_0(H)$.

ii. The induction map * sends $\bar{Z}H \rightarrow \bar{Z}G$, $I(H) \rightarrow I(G)$ and $I_0(H) \rightarrow I_0(G)$.

Proof. Part (i) is obvious. We consider (ii). Clearly $\bar{Z}H \rightarrow \bar{Z}G$. Also if $\alpha \in \bar{Z}H$, then $\alpha^*(1) = [G:H]\alpha(1)$. In particular if $\alpha(1) = 0$ then $\alpha^*(1) = 0$. Thus if suffices to show that $I(H) \rightarrow I(G)$. Since * is clearly linear we show that if χ is a character of H, then χ^* is a character of G.

Let $\chi = \chi_A$. Define A_0, a matrix function of G

to be $A_0(g) = A(g)$ if $g \in H$ and $A_0(g) = 0$ if $g \in G-H$. Let $x_1, x_2, \ldots, x_w$ be a set of right coset representatives of H with $[G:H] = w$. Define A^* to be $A^*(g) = [A_0(x_i g x_j^{-1})]$ where each pair of subscripts denotes an $n \times n$ matrix with $n = n(A)$.

We show that A^* is a representation of G. Now G permutes the right coset of H by right multiplication. If $Hx_i g = Hx_j$ we write $j = ig$ so that $Hx_i g = Hx_{ig}$. Thus $x_i g x_j^{-1} \in H$ if and only if $j = ig$. Let $g, h \in G$. Then $A^*(g)A^*(h) = [B_{ij}]$ with $B_{ij} = \sum_s A_0(x_i g x_s^{-1}) A_0(x_s h x_j^{-1})$. Now $A_0(x_i g x_s^{-1}) = 0$ unless $s = ig$ and thus $B_{ij} = 0$ unless $j = igh$. Thus if $j \neq igh$ we have $B_{ij} = 0 = A_0(x_i gh x_j^{-1})$. On the other hand if $j = igh$, then with $s = ig$ we have

$$\begin{aligned} B_{ij} &= A(x_i g x_s^{-1}) A(x_s h x_j^{-1}) \\ &= A(\,(x_i g x_s^{-1})(x_s h x_j^{-1})\,) = A(x_i gh x_j^{-1}). \end{aligned}$$

This yields $A^*(g)A^*(h) = A^*(gh)$ and hence A^* is a representation of G.

Now $\operatorname{tr} A_0(g) = \chi_0(g)$ for $g \in G$ and thus we have $\chi_{A^*}(g) = \sum_i \chi_0(x_i g x_i^{-1})$. If $y \in H$ then since χ is a class function on H, $\chi_0(y x_i g x_i^{-1} y^{-1}) = \chi_0(x_i g x_i^{-1})$. This yields easily $\chi_{A^*}(g) = |H|^{-1}\sum_{x\in G}\chi_0(xgx^{-1}) = \chi^*(g)$. This completes the proof.

The following result is known as Frobenius reciprocity.

THEOREM 16.6. (Frobenius) Let H be a subgroup of G and let $\alpha \in \bar{Z}G$, $\beta \in \bar{Z}H$. Then $[\alpha|H, \beta]_H = [\alpha, \beta^*]_G$.

Proof. We have clearly

$$[\alpha, \beta^*]_G = |G|^{-1}|H|^{-1}\sum_{g\in G}\sum_{x\in G}\alpha(g)\overline{\beta_0(x^{-1}gx)}.$$

Set $h = x^{-1}gx$ so that $g = xhx^{-1}$. Thus

$$[\alpha, \beta^*]_G = |G|^{-1}|H|^{-1}\sum_{x\in G}\sum_{h\in G}\alpha(xhx^{-1})\overline{\beta_0(h)}.$$

Now $\alpha(xhx^{-1}) = \alpha(h)$ and $\beta_0(h) = 0$ if $h \in G-H$. This yields

$$[\alpha, \beta^*]_G = |G|^{-1}\sum_{x\in G}|H|^{-1}\sum_{h\in H}\alpha(h)\overline{\beta(h)} = [\alpha|H, \beta]_H$$

and the result follows.

THEOREM 16.7. The number of irreducible characters of

G is equal to the number of conjugacy classes of G.

Proof. Let k be the number of such characters and let c be the number of classes of G. We have clearly $\dim \bar{Z}G = c$ and since the characters are linearly independent we have $c \geq k$. Let $\bar{T}G$ denote the linear subspace of $\bar{Z}G$ spanned by the characters. We show that $\bar{T}G = \bar{Z}G$ and this will yield the result.

First let G be abelian. By Corollary 15.4 all irreducible characters of G have degree 1 and by Proposition 15.7 (iv) there are $|G|$ such characters. Thus the result follows here and $\bar{T}G = \bar{Z}G$.

Now let G be arbitrary and let $g \in G$. Set $H = \langle g \rangle$ so that H is abelian. Since $\bar{T}H = \bar{Z}H$ we see that we can find $\alpha \in \bar{T}H$ with $\alpha(g) = 1$ and $\alpha(h) = 0$ if $h \in H$ and $h \neq g$. By Theorem 16.5 and the linearity of the induction map $*$ we see that $\alpha^* \in \bar{T}G$. If $w \in G$ then $\alpha^*(w) = |H|^{-1} \sum_{x \in G} \alpha_0(x^{-1}wx)$. Thus $\alpha^*(w) = 0$ if w is not conjugate to g and $\alpha^*(w) > 0$ if w is conjugate to g. This shows that the elements of $\bar{T}G$ separate the classes of G and hence $\bar{T}G = \bar{Z}G$. This completes the proof.

Let χ be a character of G. We define the kernel of χ to be $\ker \chi = \{g \in G \mid \chi(g) = \chi(1)\}$.

THEOREM 16.8. If $\chi = \chi_A$ is a character of G then $\ker \chi = \ker A$. Furthermore if $\chi_1, \chi_2, \ldots, \chi_k$ are all the irreducible characters of G then $\bigcap_i \ker \chi_i = \langle 1 \rangle$.

Proof. If $g \in \ker A$, then $A(g) = I$ and hence $\chi(g) = \chi(1)$. Conversely let $g \in \ker \chi$. Set $H = \langle g \rangle$. As in the proof of Proposition 16.3 we have
$A \mid H \sim B = B_1 + B_2 + \ldots + B_n$ where each B_i has degree 1 and $n = n(A) = \chi(1)$. Now $\chi_{B_i}(g)$ is a root of unity. Hence $|\chi(g)| = |\chi_{B_1}(g) + \chi_{B_2}(g) + \ldots + \chi_{B_n}(g)| \leq n = \chi(1)$. Since $\chi(g) = \chi(1)$ we must have equality throughout. This implies that all $\chi_{B_i}(g)$ are equal and hence we have $\chi(1) = \chi(g) = \chi(1)\chi_{B_i}(g)$. Thus $\chi_{B_i}(g) = 1$ for all i and $g \in \ker B$. Since $B(g) = I$ and $A(g)$ is conjugate to $B(g)$ we have $A(g) = I$ and $g \in \ker A$.

Now let $g \in \bigcap_i \ker \chi_i$. Then for all i, $\chi_i(g) = \chi_i(1)$. Since the characters χ_i span $\bar{Z}G$ it follows that g and

1 are conjugate in G and hence $g = 1$. This completes the proof.

If A is the unit representation of G then $n(A) = 1$ and hence A is irreducible. We denote its character by 1 or 1_G. Clearly $1_G(g) = 1$ for all $g \in G$ and if $H \subseteq G$ then $1_G | H = 1_H$.

Let G be a permutation group on $\{v_1, v_2, \ldots, v_n\}$ and let A be the associated representation. Let $g \in G$. Then the nonzero diagonal entries of $A(g)$ correspond to those v_i with $v_i g = v_i$. Hence we see easily that $\chi_A = \theta$, where $\theta(g)$ is the number of points fixed by g.

PROPOSITION 16.9. Let G be a permutation group and let θ be as above.

i. $[\theta, 1_G]$ equals the number of orbits of G.

ii. If G is transitive then $[\theta, \theta]$ is equal to the number of orbits of G_a.

In particular if G is doubly transitive then $\theta = 1_G + \chi$ where χ is an irreducible character.

Proof. Since $\theta = \bar{\theta}$, statements (i) and (ii) follow from Propositions 3.1 and 3.9. Now let G be doubly transitive and write $\theta = a_1\chi_1 + a_2\chi_2 + \ldots + a_k\chi_k$ where the a_i are nonnegative integers. We have $2 = [\theta, \theta] = a_1^2 + a_2^2 + \ldots + a_k^2$ and hence two of the a_i equal 1 and the rest are 0. Say $\theta = \chi_1 + \chi_2$. Since $[\theta, 1_G] = 1$, one of χ_1 or χ_2 is equal to 1_G and the result follows.

The final result of this section is of a different nature. Let π be a set of primes. We say $g \in G$ is a π-element if $o(g)$ is a π-number.

THEOREM 16.10. (Blichfeldt-Burnside) Let π_1 and π_2 be two sets of primes. Let G be a group with a central subgroup Z of order $|Z| \leq 2$. Suppose that every element of G/Z is either a π_1'-element or a π_2'-element. If χ is an irreducible character of G, then χ is rational on the set of all π_1-elements or the set of all π_2-elements of G.

<u>Proof</u>. Let $|G| = n$ and write $n = n_1 n_1' = n_2 n_2'$ with n_i a π_i-number and n_i' a π_i'-number. Suppose by way of contradiction that G contains π_i-elements g_i with $\chi(g_i)$ not rational for $i = 1, 2$.

Since $\chi(g_i)$ is not rational, it follows that it is not fixed by some field automorphism. Hence by Proposition 16.3 there exists integers r_i with $(r_i, n_i) = 1$ and $\chi(g_i) \neq \chi(g_i^{r_i})$. Since $(n_i, n_i') = 1$ we can find integers s_i with $s_i \equiv r_i \mod n_i$ and $s_i \equiv 1 \mod n_i'$.

Let ε be a primitive n^{th} root of unity and let τ_i be the field automorphism of $\mathbb{Q}(\varepsilon)$ given by $\varepsilon \to \varepsilon^{s_i}$. Then since $s_i \equiv r_i \mod n_i$, $\chi^{\tau_i}(g_i) = \chi(g_i^{s_i}) = \chi(g_i^{r_i}) \neq \chi(g_i)$. On the other hand suppose that h_i is a π_i'-element. Then since $s_i \equiv 1 \mod n_i'$ and $o(h_i) \mid n_i'$ we have $\chi^{\tau_i}(h_i) = \chi(h_i^{s_i}) = \chi(h_i)$.

Let $h \in G$. By assumption the image of h in G/Z is a π_i'-element for $i = 1$ or 2 and hence clearly $h = zh_i$ where $z \in Z$ and h_i is a π_i'-element. If R is the representation associated with χ then by Corollary 15.4, R(z) is a scalar matrix and hence since $z^2 = 1$, $R(z) = \pm I$ where I is the identity matrix. Thus $R(h) = \pm R(h_i)$ and

$\chi(h) = \pm \chi(h_i)$. Hence by the above we have

$\chi^{\tau_i}(h) = \pm \chi^{\tau_i}(h_i) = \pm \chi(h_i) = \chi(h)$. Thus

$$\chi(h) - \chi^{\tau_1}(h) - \chi^{\tau_2}(h) + \chi^{\tau_1 \tau_2}(h) = 0$$

and we have $\chi + \chi^{\tau_1 \tau_2} = \chi^{\tau_1} + \chi^{\tau_2}$. Clearly χ^{τ_1}, χ^{τ_2} and $\chi^{\tau_1 \tau_2}$ are irreducible and hence by the linear independence of such characters we have $\chi = \chi^{\tau_1}$ or χ^{τ_2}. This contradicts the fact that $\chi^{\tau_1}(g_1) \neq \chi(g_1)$ and $\chi^{\tau_2}(g_2) \neq \chi(g_2)$ and the result follows.

CHAPTER III

CLASSIFICATION THEOREMS

17. FROBENIUS KERNELS

We now return to our study of permutation groups.

THEOREM 17.1. (Frobenius) Let G be a Frobenius group. Then G contains a regular normal subgroup.

Proof. Let $H = G_a$. Then H is a T.I. set and $\mathfrak{N}(H) = H$.

Step 1. The induction map $*$ induces an isometry from $I_0(H)$ to $I_0(G)$. That is for all $\alpha, \beta \in I_0(H)$,

$[\alpha^*, \beta^*]_G = [\alpha, \beta]_H$. Moreover $\alpha^*|H = \alpha$.

We show first that $\alpha^*|H = \alpha$. Let $g \in H^{\#}$. Then $\alpha^*(g) = |H|^{-1} \sum_{x \in G} \alpha_0(x^{-1}gx)$. If $x^{-1}gx \in H$ then $H \cap H^x \neq \langle 1 \rangle$ and hence $x \in \mathfrak{N}(H) = H$. Since α is a class function of H this yields $\alpha^*(g) = \alpha(g)$. Now if $g = 1$, then $\alpha^*(g) = \alpha(g)$ since $\alpha(1) = 0$ by assumption. Hence $\alpha^*|H = \alpha$.

Finally by Theorem 16.6, $[\alpha^*, \beta^*]_G = [\alpha, \beta^*|H]_H = [\alpha, \beta]$ and this follows.

Step 2. Set $N = \{ g \in G \mid g = 1 \text{ or } \Theta(g) = 0 \}$. Then $N \triangle G$.

Let $\varphi_0, \varphi_1, \ldots, \varphi_k$ be the irreducible characters characters of H with $f_i = \deg \varphi_i$, the degree of φ_i. We can assume that $\varphi_0 = 1_H$. For $i \neq 0$ set $\alpha_i = f_i 1_H - \varphi_i$. Then $\alpha_i \in I_0(H)$ and $\|\alpha_i\|^2 = f_i^2 + 1$. By Frobenius reciprocity $[\alpha_i^*, 1_G]_G = [\alpha_i, 1_G|H]_H = [\alpha_i, 1_H]_H = f_i$. Thus $\alpha_i^* = f_i 1_G + \chi$ where χ is a generalized character of G orthogonal to 1_G. Since $\|\alpha_i^*\|^2 = f_i^2 + 1$ by Step 1 we see that $\alpha_i^* = f_i 1_G \pm \chi_i$, where χ_i is an irreducible character of G. Actually $\alpha_i^*(1) = 0$ implies

$\alpha_i^* = f_i 1_G - \chi_i$.

If we set $\chi_0 = 1_G$, then since $\alpha_i^*|H = \alpha_i$ we see that for all i, $\chi_i|H = \varphi_i$. Let $K = \bigcap \ker \chi_i$ so that K is a normal subgroup of G. Since $\chi_i|H = \varphi_i$ and $\bigcap \ker \varphi_i = \langle 1 \rangle$ by Theorem 16.8 we have $K \cap H = \langle 1 \rangle$. On the other hand if $g \in N$ then no conjugate of g is contained in $H^\#$ and hence $\alpha_i^*(g) = 0$. This yields $\chi_i(g) = f_i = \chi_i(1)$ and thus $g \in K$. Since $|N| = [G:H]$ we have $N = K$ and hence N is a normal subgroup of G. By definition of N we see that N is a regular normal subgroup of G. This completes the proof of the theorem.

We can now obtain several equivalent characterizations of a Frobenius group.

PROPOSITION 17.2. Let G be a group. The following are equivalent.

i. G is a Frobenius group with complement H of order m.

ii. G has a normal subgroup N with $\langle 1 \rangle < N < G$. If $g \in N^\#$, then $\mathcal{C}_G(g) \subseteq N$. Moreover $|N| = n$ and

$|G| = mn$.

iii. $|G| = mn$ with $(m, n) = 1$. If $g \in G$ then either $g^m = 1$ or $g^n = 1$. Moreover if $N = \{g \mid g^n = 1\}$ then N is a normal subgroup with $\langle 1 \rangle < N < G$.

Proof. (i) $\Rightarrow$ (ii) By Theorem 17.1, G has a regular normal subgroup N with $\langle 1 \rangle < N < G$. Suppose by way of contradiction that for some $g \in N^{\#}$, $\mathcal{L}_G(g) \nsubseteq N$. Now as we have seen $G = N \cup \bigcup_{x \in G} (H^{\#})^x$. By taking conjugates if necessary we can assume that there exists $h \in H^{\#}$ with $h \in \mathcal{L}_G(g)$. Then $h \in H \cap H^g$ and $H \cap H^g \neq \langle 1 \rangle$. By Proposition 8.2 this yields $g \in H$, a contradiction.

(ii) $\Rightarrow$ (iii) We show first that N is a Hall subgroup of G. Let P be a Sylow p-subgroup of N with $P \neq \langle 1 \rangle$ and extend it to P^*, a Sylow p-subgroup of G. Now $\mathcal{L}_G(P^{\#}) \supseteq \mathfrak{Z}(P^*)$ and thus $\mathfrak{Z}(P^*) \subseteq N$. Also $\mathcal{L}_G(\mathfrak{Z}(P^*)^{\#}) \supseteq P^*$ so $P^* \subseteq N$. Thus $P = P^*$ and N is a Hall subgroup.

We have $|N| = n$, $|G| = mn$ and hence $(m, n) = 1$. Since $N \triangle G$ we see that $N = \{g \mid g^n = 1\}$. Let $g \in G$ and suppose that $g^m \neq 1$. Then $(g^m)^n = 1$ so $g^m \in N^{\#}$. By (ii), $g \in \mathcal{L}_G(g^m) \subseteq N$ and hence $g^n = 1$.

(iii) $\Rightarrow$ (i) By the Schur-Zassenhaus theorem (Theorem 10.4) since N is clearly a normal Hall subgroup of G, there exists a complement H of N. Hence $|H| = m$, $G = HN$ and $H \cap N = \langle 1 \rangle$. Suppose that for some $g \in G$, $H \cap H^g \neq \langle 1 \rangle$. From $G = HN$ we see that we can assume that $g \in N$. Let $h \in H \cap H^g$ with $h \neq 1$. Then $h \in H$ and $ghg^{-1} \in H$ and thus $ghg^{-1}h^{-1} \in H$. Now $N \Delta G$ so $hg^{-1}h^{-1} \in N$ and hence $ghg^{-1}h^{-1} \in H \cap N = \langle 1 \rangle$. This yields $gh = hg$. Let $o(h) = m_1$, $o(g) = n_1$. Then $m_1 | m$, $m_1 \neq 1$, $n_1 | n$ and $(m_1, n_1) = 1$. Thus $o(hg) = m_1 n_1$. By (iii) since $m_1 \neq 1$ we must have $n_1 = 1$ and $g = 1$. This shows that H is a T.I. set with $\mathfrak{N}(H) = H$. By Proposition 8.2, G is a Frobenius group with complement H.

This yields the following result which allows us to use inductive methods in studying Frobenius groups.

PROPOSITION 17.3. Let G be a Frobenius group with Frobenius kernel N. Let K be a subgroup of G. If $K \nsubseteq N$ and $K \cap N \neq \langle 1 \rangle$, then K is a Frobenius group with kernel $K \cap N$. If $\langle 1 \rangle < K < N$ and $K \Delta G$, then G/K is a

Frobenius group with kernel N/K.

Proof. In the first situation we have $K > K \cap N > \langle 1 \rangle$ and $(K \cap N) \triangle K$. If $g \in (K \cap N)^{\#}$, then using (ii) of the previous result we have $\mathcal{L}_K(g) = K \cap \mathcal{L}_G(g) \subseteq K \cap N$ and thus K is a Frobenius group. The second result follows immediately from Proposition 17.2 (iii).

THEOREM 17.4. (Thompson) Frobenius kernels are nilpotent.

Proof. Let G be a Frobenius group with kernel N. We show that N is nilpotent by induction on $|G|$. By Proposition 17.3 it suffices to assume that $[G:N] = p$ for some prime p. Thus if H is a complement then $|H| = p$.

Suppose first that $\mathfrak{Z}(N) \neq \langle 1 \rangle$. If $\mathfrak{Z}(N) = N$, then certainly N is nilpotent. If $\mathfrak{Z}(N) \neq N$, then by Proposition 17.3, $N/\mathfrak{Z}(N)$ is the kernel of Frobenius group $G/\mathfrak{Z}(N)$. By induction $N/\mathfrak{Z}(N)$ is nilpotent and hence so is N.

We assume now that $\mathfrak{Z}(N) = \langle 1 \rangle$ and derive a contradiction. Certainly N is not nilpotent in this case and thus for some prime q, N does not have a normal q-complement. Suppose we can choose such a q with $q \neq 2$. Now $p \nmid |N|$ and H permutes the Sylow q-subgroups of N. Since the number of such subgroups is prime to p, there exists a Sylow q-subgroup Q which is normalized by H. Let $Q_0 = \mathfrak{Z}(Q)$ or $\mathfrak{J}(Q)$ so that Q_0 is characteristic in Q and hence is normalized by H. Therefore H normalizes $\mathfrak{N}_N(Q_0)$ and by Proposition 17.3, $K = H\mathfrak{N}_N(Q_0)$ is a Frobenius group with kernel $\mathfrak{N}_N(Q_0)$. If $\mathfrak{N}_N(Q_0) \neq N$, then by induction $\mathfrak{N}_N(Q_0)$ is nilpotent and hence has a normal q-complement. But by Theorem 14.6 this cannot occur for both $Q_0 = \mathfrak{Z}(Q)$ and $\mathfrak{J}(Q)$. Hence let Q_0 be one of these with $Q_0 \triangle N$. Since $G = HN$ we have $Q_0 \triangle G$. Now by induction N/Q_0 is nilpotent and hence $Q/Q_0 \triangle N/Q_0$. This yields $Q \triangle N$. On the other hand if N has a normal q-complement for all odd prime divisors of $|N|$, then $2 \mid |N|$ and N has a normal Sylow 2-subgroup.

We have therefore shown that for some prime q, N has a normal Sylow q-subgroup $Q \neq \langle 1 \rangle$. Clearly $Q \triangle G$ and hence $\mathfrak{Z}(Q)$ and $\mathfrak{L}(\mathfrak{Z}(Q))$ are normal in G. By

Proposition 17.2, $\mathcal{L}(\mathfrak{Z}(Q)) \subseteq N$ and since $\mathfrak{Z}(N) = \langle 1 \rangle$, $\mathcal{L}(\mathfrak{Z}(Q)) < N$. Set $\bar{G} = G/\mathcal{L}(\mathfrak{Z}(Q))$ and let $\bar{H}$ and $\bar{N}$ be the images in $\bar{G}$ of H and N. By Proposition 17.3, $\bar{G}$ is a Frobenius group and hence $\bar{G} = \bar{N} \cup \bigcup_{\bar{g} \in \bar{N}} \bar{H}^{\bar{g}}$ represents $\bar{G}$ as a disjoint union of $t+1$ subgroups with $t = |\bar{N}|$. Now G acts on $\mathfrak{Z}(Q)$ with kernel $\mathcal{L}(\mathfrak{Z}(Q))$ and hence $\bar{G}$ acts faithfully on $\mathfrak{Z}(Q)$. By Proposition 14.4, since $(t, q) = 1$, there exists an element $v \in \mathfrak{Z}(Q)^{\#}$ which is centralized by one of the groups $\bar{N}$ or $\bar{H}^{\bar{g}}$. Since $\mathfrak{Z}(N) = \langle 1 \rangle$ we cannot have v centralized by $\bar{N}$ and by Proposition 17.2 we cannot have v centralized by any $\bar{H}^{\bar{g}}$. This yields a contradiction and the result follows.

COROLLARY 17.5. A group G can be represented faithfully as a Frobenius group in at most one way.

Proof. Let G be a Frobenius group. It suffices to show that we can find the Frobenius complement up to conjugation in G. Let N be the Frobenius kernel. Then N is a normal nilpotent subgroup of G and hence $N \subseteq \text{Fit } G$.

Since $N \neq \langle 1 \rangle$, $N \trianglelefteq G$ and Fit G is nilpotent we see that $N \cap \mathfrak{Z}(\text{Fit } G) \neq \langle 1 \rangle$. If $g \in N \cap \mathfrak{Z}(\text{Fit } G)$ with $g \neq 1$ then by Proposition 17.2, $N \supseteq \mathcal{L}(g) \supseteq \text{Fit } G$ and hence $N = \text{Fit } G$. Finally the Frobenius complements are complements of Fit G and hence by Theorem 10.5 since $N = \text{Fit } G$ is a normal solvable Hall subgroup of G, the complements are unique up to conjugation.

In the special cases of Section 8 all the Frobenius kernels were abelian. We show now that this is not true in general.

PROPOSITION 17.6. Frobenius groups with nonabelian Frobenius kernels exist.

Proof. Consider the field $GF(q^n)$ with n odd and $n \neq 1$. Set

$$((a_1, a_2)) = \begin{bmatrix} 1 & a_1 & a_2 \\ 0 & 1 & a_1^q \\ 0 & 0 & 1 \end{bmatrix}$$

for $a_1, a_2 \in GF(q^n)$. Since $a \longrightarrow a^q$ is a field automorphism we have easily

$$((a_1, a_2))((b_1, b_2)) = ((a_1 + b_1, a_2 + b_2 + a_1 b_1^q)).$$

From this we see that the set of all such matrices forms a group N of order q^{2n}. Also since the automorphism $a \longrightarrow a^q$ is nontrivial for $n \neq 1$, we see that N is nonabelian.

Let d belong to the multiplicative group of $GF(q^n)$ have order $(q^n - 1)/(q-1)$. Define σ on N by $((a_1, a_2))\sigma = ((da_1, d^{1+q}a_2))$. By the above σ is an automorphism of N and hence $H = \langle \sigma \rangle$ acts on N. Set $G = N \times_\gamma H$, the semidirect product of N by H. We show now that G is a Frobenius group with kernel N.

Now G permutes the right cosets of H by right multiplication. Since $G = NH$ and $N \cap H = \langle 1 \rangle$ we see that N is a regular normal subgroup. By Proposition 4.2 it suffices to show that H acts semiregularly on $N^\#$. Suppose $\sigma^i \in H^\#$ centralizes $((a_1, a_2)) \in N$. Then

$$((a_1, a_2)) = ((a_1, a_2))\sigma^i = ((d^i a_1, d^{i(1+q)} a_2)).$$

Now since $\sigma^i \neq 1$ we have $d^i \neq 1$. Moreover $1+q$ is prime to $o(d) = (q^n - 1)/(q-1)$ since if $n = 2r+1$ then $(q^{2r}-1)(q^2-1)^{-1} \cdot (1+q) - q \cdot (q^n - 1)(q-1)^{-1} = 1$. This implies that $d^{i(1+q)} \neq 1$ and hence $a_1 = a_2 = 0$ and $((a_1, a_2))$ is the identity in N. This completes the proof.

In Proposition 8.3 we showed that if 2 divides the order of the Frobenius complement then the kernel is abelian. G. Higman has shown that there exists a function $k(p)$ with the property that if prime p divides the order of the Frobenius complement then the kernel has nilpotence class at most $k(p)$. His methods are not group theoretic in nature and therefore we will not prove this result here. However to indicate some of the techniques involved we offer the following simpler result.

THEOREM 17.7. (G. Higman) Let σ be an automorphism of an associative ring R. If σ fixes no nonzero element of R, then $R^p = \{0\}$.

Proof. Let $R(\omega)$ be the set of all formal sums $r_0 + \omega r_1 + \omega^2 r_2 + \ldots + \omega^{p-2} r_{p-2}$. We define addition and multiplication in $R(\omega)$ in the obvious way with the assumption that ω commutes with R and $1+\omega+\omega^2+\ldots+\omega^{p-1}=0$. Thus $R(\omega)$ is essentially the polynomial ring $R[x]$ modulo the ideal generated by $1+x+x^2+\ldots+x^{p-1}$. We define the action of σ on $R(\omega)$ by $(\omega^i r_i)\sigma = \omega^i(r_i\sigma)$. It is clear that σ fixes no element of $R(\omega)$ other than 0. Since $R(\omega) \supseteq R$ it suffices to show that $R(\omega)^p = \{0\}$.

Let $r \in R(\omega)$ and set

$$r^{(i)} = r + \omega^{-i} r\sigma + \omega^{-2i} r\sigma^2 + \ldots + \omega^{-(p-1)i} r\sigma^{p-1}.$$

We see easily using the fact that $\omega^p = 1$ that $r^{(i)}\sigma = \omega^i r^{(i)}$ and $pr = r^{(0)}+r^{(1)}+r^{(2)}+\ldots+r^{(p-1)}$.

Let S be the subring of $R(\omega)$ generated by all elements s with $s\sigma = \omega^i s$ for some i. We call $i = w(s)$, the weight of s. We show now that $S^p = \{0\}$. Let $s_1, s_2, \ldots, s_p$ be any p generators of S. It suffices to show that $s_1 s_2 \ldots s_p = 0$. Consider the sequence of partial sums 0, $w(s_1)$, $w(s_1)+w(s_2)$, $w(s_1)+w(s_2)+w(s_3)$, $\ldots$. There are $p+1$ terms in this sequence and hence two of them must be congruent modulo p. Thus there exists $1 \leq i \leq j \leq p$ with

$w(s_i)+w(s_{i+1})+\ldots+w(s_j) \equiv 0 \mod p$. This yields $(s_i s_{i+1} \ldots s_j)\sigma = (s_i s_{i+1} \ldots s_j)$ and hence $s_i s_{i+1} \ldots s_j = 0$. Therefore $s_1 s_2 \ldots s_p = 0$ and $S^p = \{0\}$.

Now let $r_1, r_2, \ldots, r_p \in R(\omega)$ and set $y = r_1 r_2 \ldots r_p$. As we saw above $pr_i \in S$ and hence $p^p y \in S^p = \{0\}$. Consider the additive abelian group A generated by $y, y\sigma, \ldots, y\sigma^{p-1}$. Since $p^p y = 0$ we see that A is a finite p-group. Now A is σ-invariant and $\langle\sigma\rangle$ permutes the elements of $A - \{0\}$ in orbits of size p. Hence $|A| = kp+1$. Since A is a p-group this yields $A = \{0\}$ and hence $y = 0$. This completes the proof.

The preceeding results study the regular normal subgroups of Frobenius groups. We now study the remaining 3/2-transitive permutation groups.

THEOREM 17.8. Let G be a 3/2-transitive permutation group and let N be a regular normal subgroup. If G is not a Frobenius group, then N is an elementary abelian p-group for some prime p and N is the unique minimal normal subgroup of G.

Proof. Let $H = G_a$ so that H acts as an automorphism group on N and $1/2$-transitively on $N^{\#}$. If $x \in N^{\#}$ we set $N_x = \mathcal{L}_N(H_x)$. We show first that the groups N_x form a partition of N. First $x \in N_x$ so $N = \bigcup N_x$. Now let $N_x \cap N_y \neq \langle 1 \rangle$ and let z be a common nonidentity element. Then $H_z \supseteq H_x$ and $H_z \supseteq H_y$. Since H is $1/2$-transitive, $|H_x| = |H_y| = |H_z|$ and hence $H_x = H_y$. This yields $N_x = N_y$.

Now H permutes the conjugacy classes of N and we use $H_{\langle \mathrm{Cl}\, x \rangle}$ to denote the subgroup of H fixing $\mathrm{Cl}\, x$ setwise. We show that for $x \neq 1$, $H_{\langle \mathrm{Cl}\, x\rangle} = H_x$. Certainly $H_{\langle \mathrm{Cl}\, x \rangle} \supseteq H_x$ so it suffices to obtain the reverse inclusion. Let α denote the common size of all the orbits of H on $N^{\#}$ and let $\beta = |\mathrm{Cl}\, x|$. Then $\alpha \,\big|\, |N^{\#}|$, $\beta \,\big|\, |N|$ and hence $(\alpha, \beta) = 1$. We compute the size of $(\mathrm{Cl}\, x)H$. This set is the union of the orbits of each of the elements of $\mathrm{Cl}\, x$ and hence we have $\alpha \,\big|\, |(\mathrm{Cl}\, x)H|$ and $|(\mathrm{Cl}\, x)H| \leq \alpha |\mathrm{Cl}\, x| = \alpha\beta$. On the other hand $(\mathrm{Cl}\, x)H$ is the union of conjugacy classes of the form $\mathrm{Cl}\, y$ with y the image of x under some element $h \in H$. Clearly $|\mathrm{Cl}\, y| = |\mathrm{Cl}\, x| = \beta$ and hence $\beta \,\big|\, |(\mathrm{Cl}\, x)H|$. Since $(\alpha, \beta) = 1$ this yields $|(\mathrm{Cl}\, x)H| = \alpha\beta$ and hence $(\mathrm{Cl}\, x)H$ is the union of precisely α classes of N. Thus

$[H:H_{\langle Cl\ x\rangle}] = \alpha$. Since $[H:H_x] = \alpha$ and $H_{\langle Cl\ x\rangle} \supseteq H_x$ we obtain $H_{\langle Cl\ x\rangle} = H_x$.

If x and y are conjugate in N and $x \neq 1$, then $Cl\ x = Cl\ y$ and hence $H_x = H_y$ and $N_x = N_y$. This shows that $N_x \triangle N$. Now $N = \bigcup N_x$. If $N_x = N$, then H_x centralizes N and hence $H_x = \langle 1\rangle$. In this case H acts semiregularly on $N^{\#}$, a contradiction since G is not a Frobenius group. Thus $N_x \neq N$. Clearly $N = \langle N_z \mid N_z \neq N_x\rangle$. Since $N_x, N_z \triangle N$ and $N_x \cap N_z = \langle 1\rangle$ we see that N_z centralizes N_x and hence N_x is central in N. This shows that N is abelian. Since G is primitive by Theorem 8.1, the result follows by Proposition 4.9.

18. FROBENIUS COMPLEMENTS

In this section we study the structure of Frobenius complements. Basic properties of such groups are

THEOREM 18.1. Let G be a Frobenius complement and let p, q denote distinct primes. Then

i. G contains no subgroup of type (p, p).

ii. Every subgroup of G of order pq is cyclic.

iii. If $|G|$ is even then G contains a unique element of order 2 which is therefore central.

iv. If $p > 2$ then the Sylow p-subgroups of G are cyclic. If $p = 2$ then the Sylow 2-subgroups of G are cyclic or quaternion.

v. G has a faithful irreducible $\bar{\mathbb{Q}}$-representation R such that for all $g \in G^{\#}$ the matrix $R(g)$ has no eigenvalues equal to 1.

Proof. Let L be a Frobenius group having G as a complement and let N be the Frobenius kernel. We know that N is a nilpotent normal Hall subgroup of L. Let r be a prime divisor of $|\mathfrak{Z}(N)|$ and set $V = \{x \in \mathfrak{Z}(N) \mid x^r = 1\}$. Then $V \neq \langle 1 \rangle$ is an elementary abelian r-group which is G-invariant. By Proposition 4.2, G acts semiregularly on $N^{\#}$ and hence on $V^{\#}$. If $H \subseteq G$ then H also acts semiregularly on $V^{\#}$ and of course $r \nmid |H|$. By Proposition 14.4 we cannot write H as a disjoint union of $t+1$ subgroups unless $r \mid t$.

If H is type (p,p) then H is the disjoint union of $p+1$ subgroups of order p, a contradiction and (i) follows. If H is a noncyclic group of order pq with $q > p$, then H is the disjoint union of one subgroup of order q and q subgroups of order p. This is a contradiction since $r \nmid q$ and hence (ii) follows.

Let $g \in G$ have order 2. We show that every element of V can be written as $v^{-1}(vg)$. Here we use vg to denote as usual the image of v under g. Since V is finite, it clearly suffices to show that the map $v \longrightarrow v^{-1}(vg)$ is one to one. But if $v^{-1}(vg) = w^{-1}(wg)$ then $wv^{-1} = (wv^{-1})g$ and hence $w = v$ since G acts semiregularly. Now let $x \in V$. Then for some $v \in V$, $x = v^{-1}(vg)$. Since g has order 2, $xg = (v^{-1}(vg))g = (v^{-1}g)v = (v^{-1}(vg))^{-1} = x^{-1}$. Now if $g, h \in G$ have order 2, then $xg = x^{-1}$, $xh = x^{-1}$ and hence $xgh = x$ and $gh = 1$. Therefore $g = h$ and (iii) follows.

Let P be a Sylow p-subgroup of G and let Z be a central subgroup of P of order p. If P contains another subgroup W of order p, then P contains ZW, an abelian subgroup of type (p,p), a contradiction. Thus (iv) follows from Corollary 9.8.

Now we view the action of G on V as a representation A over $GF(r)$. Clearly A is faithful and for all $g \in G^{\#}$, $A(g)$ has no eigenvalue 1. Write $\bar{A}$, the extension of A to $\overline{GF(r)}$, as $\bar{A} = B_1 + B_2 + \ldots + B_n$ where each B_i is an irreducible $\overline{GF(r)}$-representation of G. Clearly for all $g \in G^{\#}$, $B_i(g)$ has no eigenvalue 1 since the eigenvalues of a matrix are preserved under similarity. Thus (v) follows immediately from Theorem 15.11.

We now study the solvable case.

THEOREM 18.2. (Zassenhaus) Let G be a solvable Frobenius complement. Then G has a normal subgroup G_0 such that G/G_0 is isomorphic to a subgroup of $Sym(4)$ and G_0 is a Z-group. Moreover we can write $G_0 = gp\langle x, y \mid x^n = 1,\ y^m = 1,\ x^{-1}yx = y^r\rangle$. Here $(r-1, m) = (n, m) = 1$ and $r^{n/n'} \equiv 1 \mod m$ where n' denotes the product of the distinct prime factors of n.

Proof. Suppose first that the Sylow 2-subgroups of G are cyclic. Then $G = G_0$ is a Z-group. By Proposition

12.11, G is generated by elements x, y with $x^n = 1$, $y^m = 1$, $x^{-1}yx = y^r$ and $(r-1, m) = (n, m) = 1$, $r^n \equiv 1 \bmod m$. Let p and q be primes with $p \mid n$, $q \mid m$. Then $\langle x^{n/p}, y^{m/q} \rangle$ is a group of order pq and must therefore be cyclic. Thus $x^{n/p}$ centralizes all elements of $\langle y \rangle$ of prime order and hence by Proposition 9.3, $x^{n/p}$ centralizes $\langle y \rangle$. Since this is true for all $p \mid n$ we see that $x^{n/n'}$ centralizes $\langle y \rangle$ and hence $r^{n/n'} \equiv 1 \bmod m$.

Now let the Sylow 2-subgroups of G be quaternion. Let $W = \text{Fit } G$ and let W_p denote the Sylow p-subgroup of W. We will be using Fitting's theorem (Theorem 11.4) freely throughout this section without further reference to it. For $p > 2$, W_p is of course cyclic and for $p = 2$, W_p is cyclic or quaternion. Let S be a Sylow 2-subgroup of G so that $S \supseteq W_2$. There are now three cases to consider.

First let W_2 be cyclic. Then W is cyclic and since G/W acts faithfully on W we see that G/W is abelian. This implies that $S' \subseteq W$ and since S/S' is abelian of type $(2, 2)$ we see that G/W has a subgroup G_0/W of odd order with G/G_0 abelian of type (2) or $(2, 2)$. Since G_0 is clearly a Z-group, the result follows here.

Second, let W_2 be the quaternion group of order 8 and set $G_0 = \mathcal{L}(W_2)$. Then G/G_0 is contained isomorphically in Aut $W_2 \cong \text{Sym}(4)$ by Proposition 9.9. Since it is easy to see that $\mathcal{L}_S(W_2) = \mathfrak{Z}(S) = \mathfrak{Z}(W_2)$, it follows that G_0 is a Z-group and the result follows here.

Finally, let W_2 be a quaternion group of order at least 16. By Proposition 9.10, W_2 has a characteristic cyclic subgroup A of index 2. Then $A \triangle G$ and if $G_0 = \mathcal{L}(A)$ then $G_0 \triangle G$. Since Aut A is a 2-group we see that G/G_0 is a 2-group. Now $|A| \geq 8$ so clearly $[S:\mathcal{L}_S(A)] = 2$. This yields $[G:G_0] = 2$ and since $\mathcal{L}_S(A)$ is cyclic, G_0 is a Z-group and the theorem is proved.

We will need to study those solvable Frobenius complements with $\mathfrak{Z}(G)$ a 2-group. Again we let W = Fit G with W_p the Sylow p-subgroup of W. Also we let S be a Sylow 2-subgroup of G.

LEMMA 18.3. Let G be a solvable Frobenius complement with $\mathfrak{Z}(G)$ a 2-group.

i. Let $p > 2$ and let P be a Sylow p-subgroup

of G. Then $P \subseteq G'$ unless $p = 3$, $|P| = 3$ and S is the quaternion group of order 8.

ii. The $S_{2'}$ subgroups of G are cyclic.

iii. Let T be an $S_{2'}$ subgroup of G. If W_2 is not the quaternion group of order 8 then $T \triangle G$. If W_2 is the quaternion group of order 8, then either $T \triangle G$ or there exists a subgroup H of T with $[T:H] = 3$ and $H \triangle G$.

Proof. If $P \nsubseteq G'$, then by Lemma 12.10 G has a normal p-complement K. Let P^* denote the subgroup of P of order p. Let r be a prime divisor of $|K|$. Then P permutes the Sylow r-subgroups of K by conjugation and since their number is prime to p, there exists a Sylow r-subgroup R of K which is normalized by P. Let R^* be the unique subgroup of R of order r so that P normalizes R^*. Since $|R^*P^*| = rp$, R^*P^* is cyclic and P^* centralizes R^*. If R is cyclic then by Proposition 9.3, P^* centralizes R. Now by assumption $P^* \nsubseteq \mathfrak{Z}(G)$ and hence P^* cannot centralize all such subgroups. Thus for $r = 2$, P^* and hence P acts faithfully on R. The only possibility here is clearly $p = 3$, $|P| = 3$ and R quaternion of order 8. This yields (i).

By Lemma 12.9, the $S_{2'}$ subgroups of G' are cyclic. Hence (ii) follows from (i) unless S is the quaternion group of order 8 and P, a Sylow 3-subgroup of G, has order 3 with $P \not\subseteq G'$. In this exceptional case we see that there exists an $S_{2'}$ subgroup J of G' which is normalized by P. As in the above, P centralizes all elements of J of prime order and hence P centralizes J. Since J is a cyclic $3'$-group, (ii) follows.

Let T be an $S_{2'}$ subgroup of G. Then since T is cyclic it centralizes the $S_{2'}$ subgroup $W_{2'}$ of Fit G. Set $H = \mathcal{C}_T(W_2)$. Then H centralizes W and clearly $H = W_{2'} \Delta G$. Now if W_2 is cyclic or if W_2 is quaternion of order at least 16 then Aut W_2 is a 2-group and hence $H = T$. Finally if W_2 is quaternion of order 8 then $|\text{Aut } W_2| = 24 = 8 \cdot 3$ and hence either $H = T$ or $[T:H] = 3$. This completes the proof.

LEMMA 18.4. Let G be a solvable Frobenius complement

with $\mathfrak{Z}(G)$ a 2-group. Then G satisfies one of the following.

I: $M = S_{2'}(G) \triangle G$, $Q = S_2(G)$ is cyclic, $G = MQ$ and Q acts nontrivially on each Sylow p-subgroup of M.

II: $M = S_{2'}(G) \triangle G$, $Q = S_2(G)$ is a quaternion group, Q' centralizes M, $G/Q'M \cong Q/Q'$ acts nontrivially on each Sylow p-subgroup of M.

III: W_2 is quaternion of order 8, $G = W_2 P$ where $|P| = 3$ and P acts nontrivially on W_2. Hence $G \cong SL(2, 3)$.

IV: W_2 is quaternion of order 8, $W = W_2 \times M$, $\bar{G} = G/W \cong \text{Sym}(3)$, $\bar{G}/\bar{G}'$ acts nontrivially on each Sylow p-subgroup of M.

Proof. Suppose first that $S_{2'}(G) \triangle G$ and set $S_{2'}(G) = M$. Let Q be a Sylow 2-subgroup of G. Then $G = MQ$ and Q acts on M. Clearly Q must act nontrivially on each Sylow p-subgroup of M since $\mathfrak{Z}(G)$ is a 2-group and M is cyclic. If Q is cyclic, we have (I). If Q is quaternion, then since Aut M is abelian, Q' centralizes M and we have (II).

Now assume that $T = S_{2'}(G)$ is not normal. By the previous lemma we must have W_2 quaternion of order 8.

Also there is a subgroup M of G with $M \triangle G$ and $[T:M] = 3$. Here $M = \mathcal{C}_T(W_2)$. Let Q be a Sylow 2-subgroup of G. Then clearly $\mathcal{C}_Q(W_2) = \mathfrak{Z}(W_2)$ has order 2. Thus we see that $\mathcal{C}_G(W_2) = \mathfrak{Z}(W_2)M$ and hence $G/(W_2M)$ is contained isomorphically in $\text{Aut } W_2/\text{Inn } W_2 \cong \text{Sym}(3)$. Since $M \neq T$ we have $|G/(W_2M)| = 3$ or 6. If $|G/(W_2M)| = 3$, then $G = W_2T$ and hence $M \subseteq \mathfrak{Z}(G)$. This yields $M = \langle 1 \rangle$ and we have (III). It is easy to see that $G \cong SL(2, 3)$ in this case. If $|G/(W_2M)| = 6$ then since $\mathcal{C}(M) \supseteq W_2T$ we must have G/W_2T acting nontrivially on each Sylow p-subgroup of M. This yields (IV).

Now we consider the nonsolvable Frobenius complement. First we exhibit one.

PROPOSITION 18.5. $SL(2, 5)$ is a nonsolvable Frobenius complement.

Proof. We have shown that $SL(2, 5)$ is nonsolvable and by Proposition 13.7, $SL(2, 5) = gp\langle x, y, z \mid x^3 = y^5 = z^2 = 1, x^z = x, y^z = y, (xy)^2 = z\rangle$. Let F be a finite field with char $F \neq 2, 3, 5$ and assume that $\sqrt{5}, \sqrt{-1} \in F$. Define the matrices $\bar{x}, \bar{y}, \bar{z}$ as follows.

$$\bar{x} = \begin{bmatrix} -1 & 1 \\ -1 & 0 \end{bmatrix} \quad \bar{y} = \begin{bmatrix} 0 & \sqrt{-1} \\ \sqrt{-1} & (\sqrt{5}+1)/2 \end{bmatrix} \quad \bar{z} = \begin{bmatrix} -1 & 0 \\ 0 & -1 \end{bmatrix}.$$

We see easily that $\bar{x}^3 = \bar{y}^5 = \bar{z}^2 = 1$, $\bar{x}^{\bar{z}} = \bar{x}$, $\bar{y}^{\bar{z}} = \bar{y}$ and $(\bar{x}\bar{y})^2 = \bar{z}$. Thus the map $x \longrightarrow \bar{x}$, $y \longrightarrow \bar{y}$, $z \longrightarrow \bar{z}$ induces a homomorphism of $SL(2,5)$ into Aut V, where V is the 2-dimensional vector space over F. In this way $G = SL(2,5)$ acts on V. If $v \in V$, $g \in G^{\#}$ and $vg = v$ then we show that $v = 0$. It clearly suffices to assume that g has prime order p. If $p = 2$, then $g = z$ and $v = 0$ since char $F \neq 2$. If $p = 3$, then $\langle g \rangle$ is conjugate to $\langle x \rangle$ and hence we can assume that $g = x$. This yields $v = 0$ since char $F \neq 3$. Finally if $p = 5$ then we can assume that $g = y$. This yields easily $v = 0$ since char $F \neq 5$.

Set $L = VG$ and let L act by permuting the right cosets of G. We see that V is a regular normal subgroup and G acts semiregularly on $V^{\#}$. Hence L is a Frobenius group and G is a Frobenius complement.

The following result shows that $SL(2,5)$ is essentially

the unique nonsolvable Frobenius complement.

THEOREM 18.6. (Zassenhaus) Let G be a nonsolvable Frobenius complement. Then G has a normal subgroup G_0 with $[G:G_0] = 1$ or 2 such that $G_0 = SL(2,5) \times M$ with M a Z-group of order prime to 2, 3 and 5.

Proof. The proof will be by induction on $|G|$. By Proposition 17.3 we see that all nonidentity subgroups of G are Frobenius complements. Hence if $\langle 1 \rangle < H < G$, then either H is solvable and its structure is given by earlier results of this section or H is nonsolvable and it satisfies the conclusion of the theorem.

Step 1. We can assume that $G = G'$.

If $G \neq G'$, then G' is nonsolvable and hence satisfies the conclusion of the theorem. Let us first note that $SL(2,5)$ has no subgroup of index 2. Otherwise this subgroup would be a Z-group and hence would be solvable, a contradiction. This show easily that if G' has a subgroup of index 2 it has a unique such subgroup which is therefore characteristic in G'. Thus we see that $W = SL(2, 5)$ is normal in G. Let $U = \mathcal{C}_G(W)$ so that $U \Delta G$ and $|W \cap U| = 2$. If $p = 3$ or 5 divides $|U|$, let P be a Sylow p-subgroup of U and P_1 one of W. Then PP_1 is an abelian noncyclic p-subgroup of G, a contradiction. If $4 \mid |U|$ let Q be a Sylow 2-subgroup of U and Q_1 one of W. Since Q is cyclic or quaternion it contains a cyclic subgroup L of order 4. Now Q_1 is nonabelian so Q_1L is a quaternion group with a center of order at least 4, a contradiction. This clearly implies that $U = \mathfrak{Z}(W) \times M$ with $M = S_{2'}(U)$. We have M characteristic in U and hence $M \Delta G$. Moreover $2 \nmid |M|$ so M is a Z-group and $2, 3, 5 \nmid |M|$.

We have shown that G has a normal subgroup $G_0 = W \times M$ where M is of the appropriate form and $W = SL(2, 5)$. Also $\mathcal{C}_G(W) = \mathfrak{Z}(W)M$. Thus $G/\mathfrak{Z}(W)M$ is contained isomorphically in Aut W. If we show that $|\text{Aut } W| \leq 120$, then we will have $[G:G_0] = 1$ or 2 and the result will follow.

Consider the following homomorphism

$$\mathrm{Aut}\,(SL(2,5)) \longrightarrow \mathrm{Aut}\,(SL(2,5)/\mathfrak{Z}(SL(2,5)))$$
$$= \mathrm{Aut}\,(\mathrm{Alt}(5)) = \mathrm{Sym}(5).$$

Let σ belong to the kernel. Then σ fixes $W/\mathfrak{Z}(W)$ and hence for all $w \in W$ we can write $w\sigma = w(w\tau)$ where $w\tau \in \mathfrak{Z}(W)$. Since σ is a homomorphism, we see easily that τ is a homomorphism of W into $\mathfrak{Z}(W)$. But W has no subgroups of index 2 so $w\tau = 1$ for all w and $\sigma = 1$. Therefore the above homomorphism is one to one and $|\mathrm{Aut}\,(SL(2,5))| \leq |\mathrm{Sym}(5)| = 120$. Thus the result follows if $G \neq G'$ and hence we can assume $G = G'$.

Step 2. If p is a prime then all subgroups of G of order p are conjugate. The Sylow 2-subgroups of G are quaternion and all elements of G of order 4 are conjugate. Moreover $3 \mid |G|$.

The first result is of course an immediate consequence of Theorem 18.1 and the Sylow theorems. Since G is not solvable, it cannot be a Z-group and hence the Sylow 2-subgroups of G cannot be cyclic. They must therefore be quaternion. The remaining facts follow from Propositions

12.3 and 13.4.

Step 3. G has no normal subgroup of order $p > 2$ or order 4. If H is a maximal subgroup of G then $\mathfrak{Z}(H)$ is a 2-group. Moreover $|\mathfrak{Z}(G)| = 2$.

Let $P^* \Delta G$ with $|P^*| = p$ for $p > 2$ or $|P^*| = 4$ and extend P^* to P, a Sylow p-subgroup of G. Now G acts on P^* and Aut P^* is abelian so $\mathcal{L}(P^*) \supseteq G' = G$. Hence P^* is central in G. This shows that $|P^*| \neq 4$. Let $N = \mathfrak{N}_G(P)$. Then N/P centralizes P^* and hence P since P is cyclic. Therefore P is in the center of its normalizer and by Theorem 12.7, G has a normal p-complement K. Since $G/K \cong P$ we have $G > K \supseteq G'$, a contradiction.

Now let H be a maximal subgroup and suppose $\mathfrak{Z}(H)$ contains P^*, a subgroup of order p. Then $G > \mathfrak{N}(P^*) \supseteq H$ so $\mathfrak{N}(P^*) = H$. In particular $P \subseteq H$ and we have $\mathfrak{N}(P) \subseteq \mathfrak{N}(P^*) \subseteq H = \mathcal{L}(P^*)$. As above this shows that P is in the center of its normalizer, a contradiction. Choose H to contain $\mathfrak{Z}(G)$. Then $\mathfrak{Z}(G)$ is a 2-group and hence $|\mathfrak{Z}(G)| \leq 2$. By Theorem 18.1, $|\mathfrak{Z}(G)| = 2$.

Step 4. Let H be a maximal subgroup of G. If H is solvable then H has the structure of groups I, II, III or IV of Lemma 18.4. If H is nonsolvable then H satisfies one of V or VI below.

V: $H \cong SL(2,5)$.

VI: H has a subgroup H_0 of index 2 with $H_0 = SL(2,5) \times M$. Here M is cyclic and $2, 3, 5 \nmid |M|$. Also H/H_0 acts in a dihedral manner on M.

By Step 3, $\mathfrak{Z}(H)$ is a 2-group. If H is solvable, the result follows from Lemma 18.4. Suppose H is nonsolvable so that H has the form of the conclusion of the theorem. If $H = SL(2,5) \times M$, then since M is a Z-group and $2 \nmid |M|$ we see by Lemma 18.4 that if $M \neq \langle 1 \rangle$ then $\mathfrak{Z}(M) \neq \langle 1 \rangle$. Thus in this case we must have $M = \langle 1 \rangle$, $H = SL(2$, and H is type V. Suppose now that $[H:H_0] = 2$ and $H_0 = SL(2,5) \times M$. Clearly $M \triangle H$. Let L be a cyclic 2-group with $H = H_0L$ and consider ML. This latter group is a Z-group and by assumption $\mathfrak{Z}(ML)$ is a 2-group. By Lemma 18.4, M is cyclic and L acts nontrivially on each Sylow subgroup of M. Thus H/H_0 acts on M and then the action must clearly be dihedral (that is, $x \to x^{-1}$).

It follows that H is type VI.

Step 5. Let π_0 be the set consisting of 2 and those odd prime divisors p of $|G|$ with the property that G has an element of order 4p. Let a and b be two commuting elements of G. Then $\mathfrak{N}_G(\langle a \rangle) \geq \mathfrak{N}_G(\langle b \rangle) \geq \mathfrak{L}_G(b)$ if one of the following holds. Here p and q are distinct odd primes.

i. $o(b) = 4$ $\quad o(a) = p$.

ii. $o(b) = q$ $\quad o(a) = p > q$.

iii. $o(b) = q \notin \pi_0$ $\quad o(a) = p$.

By Step 3, $\langle b \rangle$ is not normal in G and hence we can choose a maximal subgroup H with $H \geq \mathfrak{N}_G(\langle b \rangle)$. If H is type I or II, then any subgroup of order $p > 2$ is normal so $H = \mathfrak{N}(\langle a \rangle)$. We see that H cannot be of type III or V since these groups do not contain commuting elements a and b of the appropriate orders. Finally let H be type IV or VI and let H_0 be the subgroup of H of index 2. Since $o(a) = p$ we have $a \in H_0$ clearly and also if $o(b) = q$ then $b \in H_0$. Let $o(b) = 4$. Since all elements of G of order 4 are conjugate, $\mathfrak{N}(\langle b \rangle)$ contains a Sylow

2-subgroup L of G. Moreover here $|L| = 16$ so we can assume that there exists $c \in L$ with $c^2 = b$. Then $c \in H$ so $b = c^2 \in H_0$. Hence in all cases $a, b \in H_0$. This together with any of the three assumptions imply that $\langle a \rangle \subseteq M$ and hence again $H = \mathfrak{N}_G(\langle a \rangle)$.

Step 6. Let H be a maximal subgroup of G. If H is type I then $Q/\mathfrak{z}(G)$ acts faithfully on each Sylow subgroup of M. If H is type II then H has a cyclic subgroup $H_0 = Q_0 \times M$ of index 2 and H/H_0 acts in a dihedral manner on M.

Suppose first that H is type I so that $H = QM$ with M normal and cyclic of odd order and Q a cyclic 2-group. Clearly $\mathfrak{z}(G) \subseteq H$ so $\mathfrak{z}(G) \subseteq Q$. If $Q/\mathfrak{z}(G)$ does not act faithfully on each Sylow subgroup of M then there exists $b \in Q$, $a \in M$ with $ab = ba$, $o(b) = 4$ and $o(a) = p > 2$. By Step 5, $H = \mathfrak{N}(\langle a \rangle) \supseteq \mathfrak{N}(\langle b \rangle)$. Since all subgroups of order 4 are conjugate, $\mathfrak{N}(\langle b \rangle)$ must contain a Sylow 2-subgroup of G which is of course quaternion. Since Q is a cyclic Sylow 2-subgroup of H this is a contradiction.

Now let H be type II so that $H = QM$ with M

normal and cyclic of odd order and Q a quaternion Sylow 2-subgroup of H. If $M = \langle 1 \rangle$, the result is clear. Assume $M \neq \langle 1 \rangle$ and let $P_1, P_2, \ldots, P_r$ be the nonidentity Sylow subgroups of M. Now Q acts nontrivially on P_i and let $Q_i = \mathcal{C}_Q(P_i)$. Since Q/Q_i is cyclic we must have $|Q/Q_i| = 2$. Set $Q_0 = Q_1$ if $|Q| = 8$ and let Q_0 be the unique cyclic subgroup of Q of index 2 if $|Q| \geq 16$. We show that $Q_i = Q_0$ for all i. Let $b_i \in Q_i$ with $o(b_i) = 4$. Since b_i centralizes an element of odd prime order in H (since $b_0 \in Q'$ if $|Q| \geq 16$) it follows by Step 5 that $\mathcal{C}(b_i) \subseteq \mathcal{N}(\langle b_i \rangle) \subseteq H$. Note that the groups $\langle b_i \rangle$ are all conjugate in G. If $|Q| \geq 16$ then $\langle b_0 \rangle \Delta H$ so $\langle b_i \rangle \Delta H$ for all i. This yields $\langle b_i \rangle = \langle b_0 \rangle$ and hence clearly $Q_i = Q_0$ here. If $|Q| = 8$ and if $Q_i \neq Q_0$, then $|\mathcal{C}(b_i)| \neq |\mathcal{C}(b_0)|$, again a contradiction. This yields the result.

Step 7. Let $p, q \in \pi_0'$. We say $p \sim q$ if either $p = q$ or $p \neq q$ and G has an element of order pq. Then $\sim$ is an equivalence relation. If π is an equivalence class, then G satisfies C_π. Every nonidentity π-element of G is contained in a unique S_π subgroup and hence the S_π subgroups of G are T.I. sets. Let S be an S_π subgroup of G. Then S is cyclic and $\mathcal{N}(S)/\mathcal{C}(S)$ is a nonidentity cyclic 2-group. Furthermore unless π is one of the exceptions tabulated below, then for all $x \in S^{\#}$, $\mathcal{C}_G(x) = \mathfrak{Z}(G)$ The exceptions are

i. $\pi = \{3\}$, $|S| = 3$ and $\mathcal{N}(S)$ is contained in a maximal subgroup H of type IV or VI with $M \neq \langle 1 \rangle$.

ii. $\pi = \{5\}$, $|S| = 5$ and $\mathcal{N}(S)$ is contained in a maximal subgroup H of type VI with $M \neq \langle 1 \rangle$.

Let us first show that $\sim$ is an equivalence relation. It is obviously reflexive and symmetric. Suppose $p \sim q$ and $q \sim r$. Then we have elements a, b, b_1, c_1 with $o(a) = p$, $o(b) = o(b_1) = q$ and $o(c_1) = r$ such that a and b commute and b_1 and c_1 commute. By Step 2, $\langle b \rangle$ and $\langle b_1 \rangle$ are conjugate. Hence a suitable conjugate c of c_1 commutes with b. We can of course assume that p, q and r are distinct. Let H be a maximal subgroup containing $\mathcal{N}(\langle b \rangle)$. Since H contains a, b, c and $p, q, r \in \pi_0'$ we see that H is not type II (since all odd primes here belong to π_0) or types III, IV, V or VI. Hence H is type I and we see that a and c commute. Hence $\sim$ is transitive and it is an equivalence relation.

Let π be an equivalence class and let $o(x) = p$ with $p \in \pi$. Suppose $x \in S$ for some S_π subgroup S of G. Since $|S|$ is odd, S is a Z-group and Theorem 18.2 yields easily $\langle x \rangle \triangle S$. Hence $S \subseteq \mathfrak{N}(\langle x \rangle)$. Therefore in order to show that x is in one and only one such S we need only look in $\mathfrak{N}(\langle x \rangle)$.

Let H be a maximal subgroup containing $\mathfrak{N}(\langle x \rangle)$. By Step 2 and the fact that $\sim$ is an equivalence relation we see that for all $q \in \pi$, $q \mid |\mathfrak{L}(x)|$. Now H cannot be type II. If H is type III or V, then since H contains a full Sylow p-subgroup of G we have $\pi = \{3\}$ or $\{5\}$, $|S| = 3$ or 5 and all results are clear.

Suppose H is type I so that $H = QM$. By Step 6 we see that $\mathfrak{L}(x) = \mathfrak{Z}(G)M$ and M is cyclic. In fact let y be any element of M of order q. Then $\mathfrak{N}(\langle y \rangle) = H$ and thus $\mathfrak{L}(y) = \mathfrak{Z}(G)M$. This shows that $q \notin \pi_0$ and that M contains a Sylow q-subgroup of G. Hence M is a cyclic S_π subgroup of G and M is the unique one containing x. If T is any other S_π subgroup then T must contain some conjugate of $\langle x \rangle$ and hence some conjugate T^g contains x. This yields all the results in this case.

Finally suppose H is type IV or VI. Since any prime divisor of $|M|$ is in π_0 we see that $\pi = \{3\}$ or $\{5\}$. Moreover if $M = \langle 1 \rangle$ then again $\mathcal{L}(x) = \mathfrak{Z}(G)\langle x \rangle = \mathfrak{Z}(G)S$. Hence the exceptions occur only if $M \neq \langle 1 \rangle$.

<u>Step 8</u>. Let $o(b) = 4$ and let H be a maximal subgroup of G with $H \geq \mathfrak{N}(\langle b \rangle)$. Then H is not type VI. Thus G does not have maximal subgroups of type VI with $M \neq \langle 1 \rangle$ and $\pi = \{5\}$ is not an exception in Step 7.

Suppose H is a maximal subgroup of G of type VI containing $\mathfrak{N}(\langle b \rangle)$. Then a Sylow 2-subgroup of G has order at least 16. Since all elements of order 4 are conjugate, $b = c^2$ for some element c. Clearly $c \in H$ so $b = c^2 \in H_0$, the subgroup of H of index 2. Since $H_0 = SL(2,5) \times M$ and $3 \nmid |M|$ we see that $3 \nmid |\mathcal{L}(b)|$.

Let J be a subgroup of H_0 of order 3. We have easily $\mathcal{L}_{H_0}(J) \geq \mathfrak{Z}(G)$ and $[\mathfrak{N}_{H_0}(J):\mathcal{L}_{H_0}(J)] = 2$ so that $4 \,\big|\, |\mathfrak{N}_{H_0}(J)|$. Now $H = H_0\mathfrak{N}_H(J)$ so $[\mathfrak{N}_H(J):\mathfrak{N}_{H_0}(J)] = 2$ and $8 \,\big|\, |\mathfrak{N}_H(J)|$. Since $|\mathrm{Aut}\, J| = 2$, this yields $4 \,\big|\, |\mathcal{L}_H(J)|$

and thus $\mathcal{L}_H(J)$ must contain an element d of order 4. This is a contradiction since b and d are conjugate in G and $3 \nmid |\mathcal{L}(b)|$. This yields the first result.

Now suppose H is a maximal subgroup of type VI with $M \neq \langle 1 \rangle$. Choose $a \in M$ of order p and let $b \in \mathcal{L}_H(M)$ with $o(b) = 4$. By Step 5, $H = \mathfrak{N}(\langle a \rangle) \supseteq \mathfrak{N}(\langle b \rangle)$, a contradiction by the above and this step is proved.

Step 9. G does not have maximal subgroups of type IV with $M \neq \langle 1 \rangle$. In particular there are no exceptions in Step 7.

Suppose H is such a maximal subgroup of G of type IV with $M \neq \langle 1 \rangle$. Let H_0 be the subgroup of H of index 2, that is $H_0 = \mathcal{L}_H(M)$. We show that if $g \notin H$ then $H_0 \cap H_0{}^g = \mathfrak{z}(G)$. If not then we can choose $b \in H_0 \cap H_0{}^g$ with either $o(b) = 4$ or $o(b) = q > 2$, q a prime. Let $a \in M$ with $o(a) = p$. Then $\mathcal{L}(b) \supseteq \langle a \rangle$ and $\langle a \rangle^g$. If $b \in M$ then $H_0 = \mathcal{L}(b) \supseteq \langle a \rangle$ and $\langle a \rangle^g$ and hence $\langle a \rangle = \langle a \rangle^g$ and $g \in \mathfrak{N}(\langle a \rangle) = H$, a contradiction. If $b \notin M$ then either $o(b) = 4$ or $o(b) = q < o(a) = p$. By Step 5, this yields $H = \mathfrak{N}(\langle a \rangle) \supseteq \mathcal{L}(b)$ and so again $\langle a \rangle = \langle a \rangle^g$ and

$g \in \mathcal{N}(\langle a \rangle) = H$, a contradiction. Thus for all $g \in G-H$ we have $H_0 \cap H_0^g = \mathfrak{Z}(G)$.

Thus we see that the number of elements in all conjugates of H_0 is equal to

$$[G:H](|H_0| - 2) + 2 = |G|/2 - 2[G:H] + 2$$
$$= |G|/2 - [G:H_0] + 2.$$

Now we note that H is a Hall subgroup of G. First let $p > 2$ divide $|H|$. Then $p \mid |H_0|$ and if $a \in H_0$ with $o(a) = p$ then by the above $\mathcal{N}(\langle a \rangle) \subseteq H$. Since the Sylow p-subgroups of G are cyclic, this shows that H contains a Sylow p-subgroup of G. Now choose $a \in M$ with $o(a) = p$ and let $b \in H_0$ with $o(b) = 4$. Then $ab = ba$ and hence by Step 5, $H = \mathcal{N}(\langle a \rangle) \supseteq \mathcal{N}(\langle b \rangle)$. Since all elements of G of order 4 are conjugate $\mathcal{N}(\langle b \rangle)$ contains a Sylow 2-subgroup of G. Hence H is a Hall subgroup. This shows that a Sylow 2-subgroup of G has order $16 = 2^4$. Now H_0 contains no element of order 8. Let $c \in H$ have order 8 and suppose b above is chosen with $b = c^2$. Then we have $\mathcal{N}(\langle c \rangle) \subseteq \mathcal{N}(\langle b \rangle) \subseteq H$. Since $\mathrm{Aut}\langle c \rangle$ is a 2-group we see that $[\mathcal{N}(\langle c \rangle) : \mathcal{L}(\langle c \rangle)] = 2$ and hence since $\langle c \rangle$ is clearly self centralizing in H, $|\mathfrak{N}(\langle c\rangle)| = 16$. Now $\langle c\rangle$ contains 4 elements of order 8 and no two distinct conjugates of $\langle c\rangle$ can have an element of order 8 in common. The conjugates of $\langle c\rangle$ therefore contribute $[G:\mathfrak{N}(\langle c\rangle)]\cdot 4 = |G|/4$ elements of order 8.

So far we have counted elements which are in conjugates of H. In fact we have

$$|\bigcup_g H^g| = |G|/4 + |G|/2 - 2[G:H] + 2$$

since any element of H of order m or 2m (with m odd) is in H_0 and any element of order 4m is in the centralizer of some element of order 4 and hence in a conjugate of H_0. Finally if the element has order 8m, then since $\mathcal{L}(c) = \langle c\rangle$ above, $m = 1$. We have by the above $|\bigcup H^g| < |G|$. If x is not in this union, then since $H \geq \mathcal{L}(b)$ for $o(b) = 4$ we see that x is a π_0'-element. Moreover since the centralizers of the Sylow p-subgroups of H are contained in H we see that $3 \nmid o(x)$.

Let π_i be an equivalence class in π_0' under $\sim$ with $3 \notin \pi_i$. By the above such a class must exist. Also by Step 8, π_i is not an exceptional case of Step 7.

Let S_i be an S_{π_i} subgroup of G and set $A_i = \mathfrak{Z}(G)S_i = \mathcal{L}(S_i)$, $N_i = \mathfrak{N}(S_i)$. By Step 7 we see that $[N_i:A_i] = 2^{\nu_i} > 1$. Since the order of the Sylow 2-subgroups of G is 2^4 and N_i/A_i is cyclic we have $2 \geq \nu_i \geq 1$. Also we see clearly that if $g \notin N_i$ then $A_i \cap A_i^g = \mathfrak{Z}(G)$. Thus the number of elements of G in all conjugates of $A_i - \mathfrak{Z}(G)$ is

$$[G:N_i](|A_i| - 2) = |G|/2^{\nu_i} - 2[G:N_i].$$

This set is of course disjoint from $\bigcup H^g$.

If $\nu_i = 1$ for some i then

$$|G|/4 + |G|/2 - 2[G:H] + 2 + |G|/2 - 2[G:N_i] \leq |G|$$

so $|G|/4 < 2[G:H] + 2[G:N_i]$ and $1/8 < 1/|H| + 1/|N_i|$. This is a contradiction since $|H| \geq 48$ and $|N_i| \geq 4 \cdot 5 = 20$. Thus for all i, $\nu_i = 2$ and

$$[G:N_i](|A_i| - 2) = |G|/4 - 2[G:N_i].$$

Now there cannot be just one equivalence class π_i with the appropriate property since then we would have $(\bigcup H^g) \cup (\bigcup(A_i - \mathfrak{Z}(G))^g) = G$ and

$$|G|/4 + |G|/2 - 2[G:H] + 2 + |G|/4 - 2[G:N_i] = |G|,$$

a contradiction. Thus if π_1 and π_2 are two such classes we see that

$$|G|/4 + |G|/2 - 2[G:H] + 2$$
$$+ |G|/4 - 2[G:N_1] + |G|/4 - 2[G:N_2] \leq |G|$$

and $|G|/4 < 2[G:H] + 2[G:N_1] + 2[G:N_2]$. Hence $1/8 < 1/|H| + 1/|N_1| + 1/|N_2|$ and since $\nu_i = 2$ we have $|N_1| \geq 8 \cdot 5$, $|N_2| \geq 8 \cdot 5$, $|H| \geq 8 \cdot 3$, a contradiction and Step 9 is proved.

Step 10. Let $o(b) = 4$ and choose H maximal in G with $H \supseteq \mathcal{N}(\langle b \rangle)$. Then H is not type I or VI. If H is type III or V then $\mathcal{L}(b) = \langle b \rangle$. If H is type IV then $\mathcal{L}(b)$ is cyclic of order 8.

Now all elements of G of order 4 are conjugate so $\mathcal{N}(\langle b \rangle)$ contains a Sylow 2-subgroup L of G. Moreover if $|L| \geq 16$ we can assume that there exists $c \in L$ with $c^2 = b$. In particular this shows that if H has a normal subgroup H_0 of index 2 and if $16 \mid |H|$, then $b \in H_0$.

Since the Sylow 2-subgroups of type I groups are cyclic we cannot have H of type I. If H is type III or V we see easily that $\mathcal{L}(b) = \mathcal{L}_H(b) = \langle b \rangle$. If H is type IV then from $b \in H_0$ we have easily $\mathcal{L}(b) = \mathcal{L}_H(b)$ cyclic of order 8. Finally by Step 8, H is not type VI.

Step 11. There exists cyclic subgroups $A_0, A_1, \ldots, A_r$ such that

i. $A_i \supseteq \mathfrak{Z}(G)$ and $|A_i| = 2m_i$, $m_i > 1$.

ii. If $i \neq j$ then $(m_i, m_j) = 1$. Also we have $|G| = 4m_0m_1 \ldots m_r$.

iii. If $N_i = \mathfrak{N}(A_i)$, then N_i/A_i is cyclic of order $2^{\nu_i} > 1$ and acts faithfully on each Sylow p-subgroup of A_i for p odd. Also $2 \mid m_0$ and $\nu_0 = 1$.

iv. $A_i - \mathfrak{Z}(G)$ is a T.I. set with normalizer N_i.

v. Every element of G is contained in some conjugate of some A_i.

vi. $|G| = 2 + |G| \sum_0^r (1 - 1/m_i)/2^{\nu_i}$.

Let $\pi_1, \pi_2, \ldots, \pi_r$ be the equivalence classes of π_0' under $\sim$. We use the results of Step 7 and Steps 8 and 9, which guarantee that the exceptions of Step 7 do not occur.

Let S_i be an S_{π_i} subgroup of G and set $A_i = S_i \mathfrak{z}(G)$. If $|S_i| = m_i$, then we see that (i), (ii), (iii) and (iv) hold for these groups.

Now we consider π_0. Let $o(b) = 4$ and let H be a maximal subgroup of G containing $\mathfrak{N}(\langle b \rangle)$. Set $A_0 = \mathfrak{L}(b)$, $N_0 = \mathfrak{N}(A_0)$ and $|A_0| = 2m_0$. If H is not type II, then by Step 10 we have all of (i), (ii), (iii) and (iv) except for the result on $|G|$ which we consider later. Suppose H is type II. Then $b \in H_0$ since among all elements of H of order 4, $|\mathfrak{L}(b)|$ must be maximal. Thus by Step 6, $H = \mathfrak{N}(\langle b \rangle)$, A_0 is cyclic, $N_0 = H$ and N_0/A_0 has order 2 and acts faithfully on each Sylow p-subgroup of A_0 for p odd. If $p \mid |A_0|$, $p > 2$ then $p \in \pi_0$. This implies that $(m_0, m_j) = 1$ for $j \neq 0$. This yields (i), (ii) and (iii) except for the fact about $|G|$. We show that if $g \notin N_0$ then $A_0 \cap A_0^g = \mathfrak{z}(G)$. If not then we can find $x \in A_0 \cap A_0^g$ with $o(x) = 4$ or $o(x) = p > 2$. Since A_0 is cyclic, this yields $A_0, A_0^g \subseteq \mathfrak{L}(x) = A_0$ since $H = \mathfrak{N}(\langle x \rangle)$. Hence $g \in \mathfrak{N}(A_0) = H$, a contradiction. Thus (iv) follows. This shows also that N_0 is an S_{π_0} subgroup of G. Since $\pi_0 \cup \pi_1 \cup \ldots \cup \pi_r$ contains all prime divisors of $|G|$,

$|N_0| = 4m_0$ and $|S_i| = m_i$ for $i \neq 0$ we have $|G| = 4m_0 m_1 \ldots m_r$.

We consider (v). Let $g \in G$ with $o(g) \neq 1$. Suppose first that $p \mid o(g)$ with $p \in \pi_i$ with $i \neq 0$. Then a suitable power x of g has order p. By Step 7, $x \in S_i^{\,h}$ for some h and $g \in \mathcal{L}(x) = \mathfrak{Z}(G)S_i^{\,h} = A_i^{\,h}$ and the result follows here. Thus we can assume that g is a π_0-element. If $o(g) = 2$ then $g \in \mathfrak{Z}(G) \subseteq A_0$. If $4 \mid o(g)$ then $g \in \mathcal{L}(c)$ where $o(c) = 4$. Since $A_0 = \mathcal{L}(b)$ and b and c are conjugate, $g \in A_0^{\,h}$. The remaining possibility is that $p \mid o(g)$ for $p > 2$. By taking conjugates we can assume that g centralizes x, an element of A_0 of order p. Also A_0 must occur with H of type II above. Then $\mathcal{L}(x) = A_0$ so $g \in A_0$ and (v) follows.

Part (vi) follows immediately from the preceeding. The contribution of all conjugates of $A_i - \mathfrak{Z}(G)$ to the $|G| - 2$ elements of $G - \mathfrak{Z}(G)$ is

$$\begin{aligned}[G:N_i](|A_i| - 2) &= |G|/2^{\nu_i} \cdot (|A_i| - 2)/|A_i| \\ &= |G|/2^{\nu_i} \cdot (1 - 1/m_i).\end{aligned}$$

The result is now clear. This completes the proof of Step 11.

Step 12. If $\nu_i = 1$ for all i above then $G \cong SL(2,5)$.

We have $|G| = 2 + |G|/2 \cdot \sum_0^r (1-1/m_i)$. Clearly $r \geq 1$. If $r = 1$ then $2/|G| = 1/2m_0 + 1/2m_1$ and this is a contradiction since $2m_i = |A_i| < |G|$.

Now let $r \geq 2$. The numbers m_0, m_1 and m_2 are relatively prime and larger than 1. Thus in some order they must be larger than 2, 3, 5 respectively. With $|G| = 4m_0 m_1 \ldots m_r$ the right hand term below strictly increases with m_i. Hence

$$1 = 2/|G| + 1/2 \cdot \sum_0^r (1 - 1/m_i)$$
$$\geq 2/120 + 1/2 \{(1-1/2) + (1-1/3) + (1-1/5)\} = 1.$$

Thus we must have equality throughout and $|G| = 120$. By Proposition 13.7, $G \cong SL(2,5)$.

Step 13. Let χ be the irreducible character of the representation of G given by Theorem 18.1 (v). Say χ has degree f. Suppose χ has d distinct algebraic conjugates $\chi^{\sigma_1}, \chi^{\sigma_2}, \ldots, \chi^{\sigma_d}$ and set $\psi = \chi^{\sigma_1} + \chi^{\sigma_2} + \ldots + \chi^{\sigma_d}$. Then ψ is a rational valued character of degree df. There exists $s \in \{0, 1, \ldots, r\}$ such that for all $i \neq s$, $\chi | A_i$ is rational. Moreover for $i \neq s$, $\varphi(2m_i) \mid f$ while for $i = s$, $\varphi(2m_s) \mid df$. Here φ is the Euler function.

Let S_i be the subgroup of A_i of index 2 for $i = 1, 2, \ldots, r$. Here we are assuming that $2 \mid m_0$. Then the groups $A_0, S_1, S_2, \ldots, S_r$ have pairwise relatively prime orders. By Step 11 and Theorem 16.10, χ is rational on all but at most one of these groups. Suppose χ is rational on S_i. If $g \in A_i$ then $g = xh$ with $h \in S_i$ and $x \in \mathfrak{Z}(G)$. Let R be the representation associated with χ. By Corollary 15.4, $R(x)$ is a scaler matrix and hence since $x^2 = 1$, $R(x) = \pm I$, where I is the identity matrix. Thus $R(g) = \pm R(h)$, $\chi(g) = \pm \chi(h)$ and hence χ is rational on A_i. This proves the first part of this step.

Suppose χ is rational on A_i and let $A_i = \langle g \rangle$. Then $\chi \mid A_i$ is a sum of linear characters of A_i. Let ε be a primitive $2m_i{}^{th}$ root of unity. Then clearly every irreducible representation of A_i is essentially a homomorphism of A_i into $\langle \varepsilon \rangle$ and this is uniquely determined by the image of g. If λ occurs as a constituent of $\chi \mid A_i$ then $\lambda(g)$ must be a primitive $2m_i{}^{th}$ root of unity. Otherwise some nonidentity power of g would have an eigenvalue 1 in the representation R and this contradicts Theorem 18.1 and the choice of R. Hence at most $\varphi(2m_i)$ distinct λ's can occur. If λ occurs, then it occurs with multiplicity $[\chi|A_i, \lambda]_{A_i}$. If σ is a field automorphism of $\mathbb{Q}(\varepsilon)$ then since $\chi|A_i$ is rational we have $[\chi|A_i, \lambda^\sigma] = [\chi|A_i, \lambda]$. Now all the λ^σ are distinct for distinct σ and there are $\varphi(2m_i)$ of these. Thus $\chi|A_i = a(\lambda_1 + \lambda_2 + \ldots + \lambda_w)$ with $w = \varphi(2m_i)$. Evaluating at the identity yields $f = \chi(1) = a\varphi(2m_i)$ and $\varphi(2m_i) \mid f$.

If $i = s$, then $\psi|A_i$ is rational. The same argument as above shows that $\varphi(2m_s)$ divides $\psi(1) = df$ in this case.

<u>Step 14</u>. By Step 2, $3 \mid |G|$ and hence $3 \mid m_t$ for some t. In this case $f \cdot (df/\varphi(2m_t)) < 6$.

As above $\psi|A_t = df/\varphi(2m_t) \cdot (\lambda_1 + \lambda_2 + \ldots + \lambda_w)$ where $w = \varphi(2m_t)$. Hence since $\psi(x) = \pm df$ for $x \in \mathfrak{Z}(G)$, we have

$$\begin{aligned}\sum_{g \in A_t - \mathfrak{Z}(G)} \psi(g)\overline{\psi(g)} &= |A_t| \, [\psi|A_t, \psi|A_t]_{A_t} - 2(df)^2 \\ &= 2m_t \, (df)^2/\varphi(2m_t) - 2(df)^2 \\ &= 2(df)^2 \{m_t - \varphi(2m_t)\}/\varphi(2m_t).\end{aligned}$$

We sum this over all conjugates of $A_t - \mathfrak{Z}(G)$ using the fact that this is a T.I. set. Also N_t/A_t acts faithfully on the cyclic Sylow 3-subgroup of A_t so $[N_t:A_t] = 2$. Since $[\Psi, \Psi] = d$, this yields

$$d|G| = |G|[\Psi,\Psi] = \sum_{g \in G} \Psi(g)\overline{\Psi(g)}$$
$$> |G|/|N_t| \cdot 2(df)^2 \{m_t - \varphi(2m_t)\}/\varphi(2m_t)$$

or $1 > f\cdot(df)/\varphi(2m_t)\cdot (m_t - \varphi(2m_t))/2m_t$. Now $3 \mid m_t$ so $\varphi(2m_t) \leq 2m_t(1-1/2)(1-1/3) = 2m_t/3$ and hence we have $(m_t - \varphi(2m_t))/2m_t \geq 1/6$. This yields $6 > f\,(df)/\varphi(2m_t)$.

Step 15. Proof of the theorem.

Let L be a Sylow 2-subgroup of G. Then $\chi|L$ is a character of L and as such it is a sum of irreducible characters of L. If some constituent has degree 1 then L' is in its kernel and thus some nonidentity element of L has an eigenvalue 1 in R, a contradiction. Thus by Theorem 15.10 all such constituents have even degree and hence $2 \mid f$. We have $f\cdot(df)/\varphi(2m_t) < 6$ and $\varphi(2m_t) \mid df$ so $f = 2$ or 4.

Suppose first that $f = 2$. For any i, let $A_i = \langle g \rangle$.

By Maschke's theorem (Theorem 15.1) we can write

$R(g) = \begin{bmatrix} a & 0 \\ 0 & b \end{bmatrix}$ with $a \neq b$ since $g \notin \mathfrak{Z}(G)$. It is easy to see that if the matrix $\begin{bmatrix} c & d \\ e & f \end{bmatrix}$ normalizes $\langle R(g) \rangle$ then the square of the matrix centralizes $R(g)$. Since R is faithful this shows that $[N_i : A_i] = 2$ for all i. By Step 12, $G \cong SL(2,5)$ and the result follows.

We can assume that $f = 4$ and some $\nu_i > 1$ and derive a contradiction. We have $1 = 2/|G| + \sum_0^r (1 - 1/m_i)/2^{\nu_i}$. Let us note that we cannot have $r = 0$ or 1. The $r = 0$ case is clear. If $r = 1$ we have since $\nu_i \geq 1$, $1/2^{\nu_0} m_0 + 1/2^{\nu_1} m_1 \leq 2/|G|$, a contradiction since $2^{\nu_i} m_i = |N_i|/2 < |G|$. Thus we must have $r \geq 2$.

Let s and t be as above. If $s \neq t$, then $\varphi(2m_t) \mid f$ and $f = 4$ yields by Step 14, $d = 1$. Hence for all $i \neq t$, $\varphi(2m_i) \mid 4$. If $s = t$, then certainly for all $i \neq t$, $\varphi(2m_i) \mid 4$. Now the possibilities for $\varphi(2m_i) \mid 4$ and $3 \nmid m_i$ are $m_i = 2, 4, 5$. Since $r \geq 2$, this yields $r = 2$ and $t \neq 0$ and thus if we set $t = 1$ we have $m_0 = 2$ or 4, $m_2 = 5$. Now some $\nu_i \geq 2$ so by Step 11, $\nu_0 = 1$, $\nu_1 = 1$, $\nu_2 = 2$. The above counting equation now becomes easily

$1/2m_0 + 1/2m_1 + 1/4m_2 = 2/|G| + 1/4$. Since $2m_1 < |G|$ and $4m_2 < |G|$ we cannot have $m_0 = 2$. Thus $m_0 = 4$, $m_2 = 5$, $|G| = 4 \cdot 4 \cdot 5 \cdot m_1$ and we have from the above $1/8 + 1/2m_1 + 1/20 = 1/40m_1 + 1/4$. This yields $m_1 = 19/3$, a contradiction. Thus the theorem is proved.

If G is a Frobenius complement then every subgroup of G of order p^2 or pq is cyclic. However the converse is not true. For example the group SL(2, 17) satisfies the above yet this group is not a Frobenius complement since $|SL(2,5)| = 120$ does not divide $|SL(2,17)|$. On the other hand it is easy to show that if G is solvable then the above condition is in fact necessary and sufficient for G to be a Frobenius complement.

19. SOLVABLE DOUBLY TRANSITIVE GROUPS

In this section we classify the solvable doubly transitive permutation groups. We start by considering the action of a group G on a vector space V over GF(q). We use additive notation in V. Two examples will be of particular interest to us.

First suppose V is the additive group of $GF(q^n)$. We define $T(q^n)$ to be the set of semilinear transformations of the form $x \to ax^\sigma$ with $a \in GF(q^n)$, $a \neq 0$ and σ a field automorphism. We see easily that $T(q^n)$ is solvable, in fact metacyclic, and $|T(q^n)| = n(q^n-1)$. Moreover $T(q^n)$ acts transitively on $V^\#$.

Now let V be a 2-dimensional space over $GF(q^n)$. We define $T_0(q^n)$ to be the set of linear transformations of the form $[x, y] \to [x, y]\begin{bmatrix} a & 0 \\ 0 & \pm a^{-1} \end{bmatrix}$ or of the form $[x, y] \to [x, y]\begin{bmatrix} 0 & a \\ \pm a^{-1} & 0 \end{bmatrix}$ with $a \in GF(q^n)$, $a \neq 0$. We see easily that $T_0(q^n)$ is solvable and $|T_0(q^n)| = 4(q^n-1)$ if $q \neq 2$ and $|T_0(q^n)| = 2(q^n-1)$ if $q = 2$. Furthermore, if $q \neq 2$ then $T_0(q^n)$ acts half transitively on $V^\#$.

Suppose G acts faithfully on V and let $L = VG$ be the semidirect product of V by G. Then L permutes the right cosets of G faithfully and V is a regular normal subgroup. Thus if G is k-transitive on $V^\#$ then L is a $(k+1)$-transitive permutation group. Moreover since V is regular we can think of L as permuting the points of V.

Applying this argument to the above examples we obtain two permutation groups of interest.

First if V is the additive group of $GF(q^n)$, then $S(q^n)$ is the set of transformations $x \to ax^{\sigma} + b$ with $a, b \in GF(q^n)$, $a \neq 0$ and σ a field automorphism. This is a solvable 2-transitive group of order $nq^n(q^n-1)$ and of degree q^n.

Now let V be the two dimensional space over $GF(q^n)$ and let $S_0(q^n)$ be the set of transformations of the form

$$[x, y] \to [x, y] \begin{bmatrix} a & 0 \\ 0 & \pm a^{-1} \end{bmatrix} + [b, c]$$

$$[x, y] \to [x, y] \begin{bmatrix} 0 & a \\ \pm a^{-1} & 0 \end{bmatrix} + [b, c]$$

with $a, b, c \in GF(q^n)$ and $a \neq 0$. If $q \neq 2$, then this is a solvable $3/2$-transitive group of order $4(q^n-1)q^{2n}$ and of degree q^{2n}.

The next result follows immediately from Theorem 8.1 and Proposition 4.9.

PROPOSITION 19.1. Let G act faithfully on vector space

V and suppose that G acts 1/2-transitively on $V^{\#}$. Then either G acts semiregularly on $V^{\#}$ or G acts irreducibly on V.

We now list several basic results which consider the case in which G is a p-group.

THEOREM 19.2. (Roquette) Let p-group G act faithfully and irreducibly on vector space V of order q^n. Suppose that G is not cyclic, quaternion, dihedral or semidihedral. Then G has a subgroup H of index p such that we can write V as a direct sum $V = V_1 + V_2 + \dots + V_p$ where each V_i is an H-invariant subspace. Further H does not act faithfully on any V_i and if $g \in G-H$ then $V_i g = V_{i'}$ where the permutation $i \rightarrow i'$ is a p-cycle.

Proof. Let U be the normal abelian subgroup of G of type (p, p) guaranteed by Proposition 9.5. Now we must have $q \neq p$ since otherwise $L = VG$ is a p-group, $\mathfrak{Z}(L) \cap V \neq \langle 1 \rangle$ and certainly G cannot act faithfully and irreducibly. By Corollary 15.4, $\mathfrak{Z}(G)$ is cyclic and hence $J_0 = U \cap \mathfrak{Z}(G)$ has order p. Let $J_1, J_2, \ldots, J_p$ be the remaining subgroups of U of order p. These are not normal in G. Since $U \Delta G$, G permutes these subgroups by conjugation in one cycle of length p. Let $H = \mathfrak{N}(J_1)$. Then clearly J_0 and J_1 are central in H so J_i is central in H for all i and $H = \mathfrak{N}(J_i)$ for all $i \neq 0$. We set $V_i = \mathfrak{C}_V(J_i)$ for $i \neq 0$. Since $J_i \Delta H$, V_i is an H-invariant subspace.

Now $J_0 \Delta G$ and G acts faithfully and irreducibly so $\mathfrak{C}_V(J_0) = \langle 0 \rangle$. We show that the subspaces V_i direct sum. Suppose we have shown that the direct sum $V_1 + V_2 + \ldots + V_k$ exists and let $x \in (V_1 + V_2 + \ldots + V_k) \cap V_{k+1}$ with $x = x_1 + x_2 + \ldots + x_k$ where $x_i \in V_i$. Now V_i is H-invariant and hence is invariant under $J_{k+1} = \langle h \rangle$. Thus $x = xh = x_1 h + x_2 h + \ldots + x_k h$ and hence $x_i h = x_i$. This shows that x_i is fixed by $\langle J_i, J_{k+1} \rangle = U$ and so $x_i = 0$ and $x = 0$. Therefore $V_1 + V_2 + \ldots + V_{k+1}$ exists and hence $W = V_1 + V_2 + \ldots + V_p$ exists. If $g \in G$-H then since $J_i^g = J_{i'}$ we have $V_i g = V_{i'}$ and hence W is a G-invariant subspace. Since $U = J_0 \cup J_1 \cup \ldots \cup J_p$ is a disjoint union of $p+1$ subgroups and $\mathcal{L}_V(J_0) = \langle 0 \rangle$ we see by Proposition 14.4 that $\mathcal{L}_V(J_i) \neq \langle 0 \rangle$ for some $i \neq 0$. Hence $W \neq \langle 0 \rangle$ and since G acts irreducibly on V, $W = V$. This proves the result.

LEMMA 19.3. Let p and q be primes with $p^m - q^n = 1$. Then either $p = 2$, $n = 1$ and $q = 2^m - 1$ is a Mersenne prime, or $q = 2$, $m = 1$ and $p = 2^n + 1$ is a Fermat prime, or $p = 3$, $m = 2$, $q = 2$, $n = 3$.

Proof. We must have of course p or q even. Suppose first that $p = 2$. Thus $2^m = q^n + 1$. If n is even then since q is odd, $q^n \equiv 1 \mod 4$ and $2^m \equiv 2 \mod 4$, a contradiction. Thus n is odd and so we have $2^m = (q+1)(q^{n-1} - q^{n-2} + \dots + 1)$. Now $(q^{n-1} - q^{n-2} + \dots + 1)$ is the sum of an odd number of terms with q odd and hence this expression is odd. Since it divides 2^m, it is equal to 1. This yields $n = 1$ and the result follows here.

Now let $q = 2$ so that we have as above $2^n = p^m - 1 = (p-1)(p^{m-1} + p^{m-2} + \dots + 1)$. If m is odd, then again this latter factor must equal 1 and so $m = 1$. Now let $m = 2t$ be even so that $2^n = (p^t - 1)(p^t + 1)$. Thus $p^t - 1$ and $p^t + 1$ are numbers which are 2 apart and which are both powers of 2. This yields $p^t + 1 = 4$, $p^t - 1 = 2$, $t = 1$, $p = 3$ and the result follows.

PROPOSITION 19.4. Let p-group G act faithfully on vector space V of order q^n and transitively on $V^\#$. Then we have one of the following.

i. $q = 2$, $p = 2^n - 1$, $|G| = p$.

ii. $p = 2$, $q = 2^m + 1$, G is cyclic of order 2^m, $n = 1$.

iii. $p = 2$, $q = 3$, $n = 2$, G is cyclic or quaternion of order 8.

iv. $p = 2$, $q = 3$, $n = 2$, G is semidihedral of order 16.

Proof. Let H be the subgroup of G fixing a vector. Then $p^m = [G:H] = |V^\#| = q^n - 1$ and the previous lemma applies. Suppose first that $q = 2$. Then $m = 1$ and $p = 2^n - 1$ is a Mersenne prime. Since $[G:H] = p$, $H \Delta G$

and hence H fixes every vector of V. This yields $H = \langle 1 \rangle$ and we have (i).

Now let $p = 2$. If $n = 1$ then clearly G is cyclic so $H \triangle G$ and $H = \langle 1 \rangle$. This yields (ii). The remaining possibility is $p = 2$, $m = 3$, $q = 3$, $n = 2$. Thus $[G:H] = 8$ and $G \subseteq GL(2, 3)$. Let S be a Sylow 2-subgroup of $GL(2, 3)$ containing G so that $|S| = 16$. Suppose now that $H = \langle 1 \rangle$. Then G is semiregular and hence is either cyclic or quaternion. This yields (iii). Finally let $|H| > 1$, so that clearly $G = S$. This will yield (iv) provided we show that S is semidihedral or equivalently that $GL(2, 3)$ contains a semidihedral group of order 16. Set $g, h \in GL(2, 3)$ with $g = \begin{bmatrix} 1 & -1 \\ 1 & 1 \end{bmatrix}$, $h = \begin{bmatrix} 1 & 0 \\ 0 & -1 \end{bmatrix}$. Then $g^8 = h^2 = 1$, $h^{-1}gh = g^3$ so $\langle g, h \rangle$ is semidihedral of order 16 and the result follows.

PROPOSITION 19.5. Let G act faithfully on vector space V of order q^n and suppose that for all $x \in V^\#$, $|G_x| = 2$. If G has a central element of order 2, then $n = 2r$ and G contains precisely $q^r + 1$ noncentral elements of order 2.

Proof. Clearly G acts $1/2$-transitively but not semiregularly on $V^{\#}$. By Proposition 19.1, G acts irreducibly on V. Let z be the given central element of G of order 2. Since $\mathcal{L}_V(z)$ is G-invariant and G acts faithfully it follows that $\mathcal{L}_V(z) = \langle 0 \rangle$ and hence the linear transformation $z-1$ is nonsingular. From $(z-1)(z+1) = (z^2-1) = 0$ we have $z+1 = 0$ and z acts like -1. For convenience we will denote this element by -1. This shows that $q \neq 2$.

Let I denote the set of noncentral involutions (elements of order 2) of G. From the fact that $|G_x| = 2$ for all $x \in V^{\#}$ we have the disjoint union $V = \bigcup_{g \in I} \mathcal{L}_V(g)$. If $|I| \leq 2$, then V is the union of two proper subspaces, a contradiction. Hence $|I| \geq 3$. Let $g \in I$. Then $1 = (1-g)/2 + (1+g)/2$, a sum of linear transformations, induces easily the direct sum $V = \mathcal{L}_V(g) + \mathcal{L}_V(-g)$. Since $|I| \geq 3$ we can find $h \in I$ with $h \neq g, -g$. Moreover we can assume that $|\mathcal{L}_V(h)| \geq |\mathcal{L}_V(-h)|$. From $V = \mathcal{L}_V(h) + \mathcal{L}_V(-h)$, $\mathcal{L}_V(h) \cap \mathcal{L}_V(g) = \langle 0 \rangle$ and $\mathcal{L}_V(h) \cap \mathcal{L}_V(-g) = \langle 0$ we obtain easily $n = 2r$ and $|\mathcal{L}_V(g)| = q^r$. The disjoint union then yields $q^{2r}-1 = |V^{\#}| = |I||\mathcal{L}_V(g)^{\#}| = |I|(q^r-1)$.

Hence $|I| = q^r + 1$ and the result follows.

Our first main result is

THEOREM 19.6. Let p-group G act faithfully on vector space V of order q^n and suppose that G acts 1/2-transitively on $V^{\#}$. Then we have one of the following possibilities.

i. G is cyclic or quaternion and G acts semiregularly.

ii. $n = 2$, $q = 2^m - 1$ is a Mersenne prime and G is dihedral of order 2^{m+1} or semidihedral of order 2^{m+2}.

iii. $n = 2$, $q = 2^m + 1$ is a Fermat prime and $G = T_0(q)$.

iv. $n = 4$, $q = 3$, and G is a 2-group.

Proof. We proceed in a series of steps.

Step 1. We consider G cyclic or quaternion.

If G acts semiregularly then G is cyclic or quaternion by Theorem 18.1. We therefore assume for the remainder of this proof that G does not act semiregularly on $V^{\#}$ and hence G acts irreducibly on V. If J is a central subgroup of order p then $\mathcal{L}_V(J)$ is a G-invariant subspace. Hence $\mathcal{L}_V(J) = \langle 0 \rangle$. If G is cyclic or quaternion and if $g \in G^{\#}$ then some power of g belongs to $J^{\#}$. Thus in this case G acts semiregularly and we have (i).

Step 2. We consider G dihedral or semidihedral.

Suppose that G is dihedral of order 2^{m+1} or semidihedral of order 2^{m+2}. Then G has a normal cyclic subgroup A of index 2. If $g \in A^{\#}$ then some power of g is in $\mathfrak{Z}(G)^{\#}$ and hence by the above g fixes no element of $V^{\#}$. Thus if $x \in V^{\#}$ then $G_x \cap A = \langle 1 \rangle$ and $|G_x| = 1$ or 2. Since G acts 1/2-transitively but not semiregularly we have $|G_x| = 2$ for all $x \in V^{\#}$ and Proposition 19.5 applies. Let I denote the set of noncentral involutions of G. If G is dihedral we see easily that $I = G - A$ while if G is semidihedral then I consists of half the elements of $G-A$. Thus in both cases $|I| = 2^m$. By Proposition 19.5, $n = 2r$ and $2^m = |I| = q^r + 1$. By Lemma 19.3, $r = 1$, $q = 2^m - 1$ is a Mersenne prime and we have (ii).

Step 3. We now assume that G is not cyclic, quaternion, dihedral or semidihedral. Let H be the subgroup of G of index p given by Theorem 19.2. Write $V = V_1 + V_2 + \dots + V_p$ where each V_i is an H-subspace and the V_i are permuted cyclically by G/H. Let K_i be the kernel of the action of H on V_i. Then the groups K_i are all conjugate in G and $|K_i| > 1$. If $x \in V_i^{\#}$ then $G_x = H_x$. Hence H/K_i acts 1/2-transitively on $V_i^{\#}$. Moreover we have $p = 2$.

We need only show the last two statements. If $g \in G-H$ and $x \in V_i^{\#}$ then $xg \in V_{i'}^{\#}$ where $i \to i'$ is a p-cycle. Hence $g \notin G_x$. This show that $G_x \subseteq H$ and hence $H_x = G_x$. Thus for all $x \in V_i^{\#}$, $|H_x| = |G_x|$ is a constant and so H/K_i acts 1/2-transitively on $V_i^{\#}$. Suppose $p > 2$ and let $x \in V_i^{\#}$, $y \in V_j^{\#}$ with $i \neq j$. If $g \in G$ fixes $x+y$ then since $(x+y)g \in V_{i'} + V_{j'}$ we must have either $i = i'$, $j = j'$ and $g \in H$ or $i = j'$, $j = i'$ and $g^2 \in H$. Thus in either case since $p > 2$, $g \in H$. Since each V_i is an H-module we must have $xg = x$, $yg = y$ and hence $G_{x+y} = G_x \cap G_y$. Now $|G_x| = |G_{x+y}| = |G_y|$ so $G_x = G_{x+y} = G_y$. Fix x and let y vary. Then G_x centralizes all V_j with $j \neq i$. Since

$G_x = G_y$ and G_y centralizes V_i we see that G_x fixes all of V and $G_x = \langle 1 \rangle$. Now G is 1/2-transitive so it is semiregular and hence G is cyclic, a contradiction. Thus $p = 2$.

Step 4. We assume for the remainder of this proof that $p = 2$. Then H/K_i acts transitively on $V_i^{\#}$.

Let g be a fixed element of G-H. Let $x \in V_1^{\#}$ so that $G_x = H_x$. Let W be the centralizer of G_x in V_2. If $W = V_2$ then $G_x \subseteq K_2$. Now $K_1 \subseteq G_x$ and $K_1 \cap K_2 = \langle 1 \rangle$ since $K_1 \cap K_2$ is the kernel of the action of H on V and thus $K_1 = K_2 = \langle 1 \rangle$, $G_x = \langle 1 \rangle$ and G is semiregular on $V^{\#}$, a contradiction. Therefore W is a proper subspace of V_2. Let $y \in V_2 - W$. If $G_{x+y} \subseteq H$ then as in the preceding step, $G_x = G_{x+y} = G_y$ and G_x centralizes y, a contradiction. Thus we can find $gh \in G_{x+y}$ with $h \in H$. Clearly $xgh = y$ and $ygh = x$ and thus $y \in (xg)H$, the orbit of $xg \in V_2$ under H. Thus $|(xg)H| \geq |V_2 - W| > 1/2 \cdot |V_2^{\#}|$. Since H/K_2 acts 1/2-transitively on $V_2^{\#}$ we must have $|(xg)H| \,\big|\, |V_2^{\#}|$ and hence $(xg)H = V_2^{\#}$. This shows that H/K_2 is transitive on $V_2^{\#}$. Similarly H/K_1 is transitive on $V_1^{\#}$.

Step 5. Since $K_2 = K_1^g$ we have $H/K_1 \simeq H/K_2$. Also $|V_1| = |V_2|$. Now Proposition 19.4 applies to H/K_i. Certainly (i) of that proposition is not applicable. If H/K_i is type (iii) or (iv) then $|V_i| = 3^2$, $|V| = 3^4$ and we have part (iv) of this theorem. If H/K_i is type (ii) then $G = T_0(q)$ with $q = 2^m+1$ and the result follows.

We need only consider the last statement. We suppose H/K_i is cyclic of order 2^m and acts semiregularly on $V_i^\#$. Here $|V_i| = q = 2^m+1$ and if $x \in V_i^\#$ then we have $G_x = H_x = K_i$. Let $x \in V_1^\#$, $y \in V_2^\#$. Then certainly $G_{x+y} \cap H = H_x \cap H_y = K_1 \cap K_2 = \langle 1 \rangle$. Since $[G:H] = 2$ this yields $|G_{x+y}| \leq 2$ and since G is not semiregular we have $|G_v| = 2$ for all $v \in V^\#$. In particular we see that $|K_1| = |K_2| = 2$. Now $K_i \triangle H$ and $|K_i| = 2$ so K_i is central in H. Since H/K_i is cyclic, this implies that H is abelian and in fact H is abelian of type $(2, 2^m)$.

Let I denote the set of noncentral involutions of G. By Proposition 19.5 $|I| = q+1 = 2^m+2$ since $n = 2$. Certainly $|I \cap H| = 2$ so $|I-(I \cap H)| = 2^m$. Let g be a fixed element of $G-H$ of order 2. If $h \in H$ we see that $(gh)^2 = 1$ if and only if $g^{-1}hg = h^{-1}$. Let $D = \{h \in H \mid h^g = h^{-1}\}$. Since

H is abelian, D is a subgroup of H and by the above $|D| = 2^m$. Now $K_1{}^g = K_2$ so $K_1 \cap D = \langle 1 \rangle$. By order considerations $H = K_1D$ and hence clearly $D = \langle h \rangle$ is cyclic. Let $K_1 = \langle k \rangle$.

Let $v_1 \in V_1{}^{\#}$ and set $v_2 = v_1 g \in V_2{}^{\#}$. Then $\{v_1, v_2\}$ is a basis for V over $GF(q)$. With respect to this basis the generators g, h, k have the following forms. Here we use the fact that $g^2 = k^2 = 1$.

$$g = \begin{bmatrix} 0 & 1 \\ 1 & 0 \end{bmatrix} \qquad k = \begin{bmatrix} 1 & 0 \\ 0 & -1 \end{bmatrix} \qquad h = \begin{bmatrix} a & 0 \\ 0 & b \end{bmatrix}$$

Since $g^{-1}hg = h^{-1}$ we have clearly $b = a^{-1}$. Thus $G = T_0(q)$ and the theorem is proved.

It is not hard to find the form of all groups in category (iv). One is $T_0(3^2)$. The other is the direct product of the dihedral and quaternion groups of order 8 with their centers identified.

It is convenient now to consider the automorphisms of the groups G which occur above.

PROPOSITION 19.7. Let G be dihedral, semidihedral or

$T_0(q)$ with $q = 2^m + 1$. Then with the exception of $T_0(5)$, Aut G is a 2-group.

<u>Proof</u>. First let G be dihedral or semidihedral so that G has a cyclic subgroup A of index 2. It is easy to see that A is the unique such subgroup so A is in fact characteristic in G. Now G has two generators so $W = G/\mathrm{Fr}\, G$ has order 4. If α is an automorphism of G of odd order then $\langle \alpha \rangle$ acts faithfully on W by Theorem 11.17 and α fixes $A/\mathrm{Fr}\, G$. Thus clearly $\alpha = 1$.

Now let $G = T_0(q)$ with $q = 2^m + 1$. If $q = 3$ then $T_0(q)$ is dihedral so we assume that $q > 5$. Let G have generators g, h, k as above and let $H = \langle k, h \rangle$ so that H is an abelian subgroup of G of index 2. Suppose that G has another abelian subgroup L of index 2. Then $G = HL$ and $[G:Z] = 4$ where $Z = H \cap L$. Since $\mathcal{L}(Z)$ contains H and L, Z is central in G and G has class 2. Now $((h, g), g) = h^{-4} \neq 1$ since $2^m > 4$ and this is clearly a contradiction. Thus H is characteristic in G. Let α be an automorphism of G of odd order. Then $\langle \alpha \rangle$ acts faithfully on $W = G/\mathrm{Fr}\, G$, an elementary abelian group of order 8. Now $H/\mathrm{Fr}\, G = V$ is an $\langle\alpha\rangle$-invariant subspace of W of order 4 and hence by Maschke's theorem, $W = V + V_1$ where V_1 is $\langle\alpha\rangle$-invariant. Since $|V_1| = 2$, α centralizes V_1. Thus $\langle\alpha\rangle$ acts faithfully on V and hence on H. Let $H_0 = \{x \in H \mid x^2 = 1\}$ and let $H_1 = \{x \in H \mid x = y^2 \text{ with } y \in H\}$. Then H_0 and H_1 are $\langle\alpha\rangle$-invariant and in fact by Corollary 14.3, $\langle\alpha\rangle$ acts faithfully on H_0. Now $|H_0| = 4$ and α must fix $H_0 \cap H_1$ a subgroup of order 2. Hence $\alpha = 1$ and the result follows.

PROPOSITION 19.8. Let G act faithfully on vector space V of order q^n. Suppose A is a normal cyclic subgroup of G which acts irreducibly on V. Then we can identify V with the additive group of $GF(q^n)$ in such a way that $G \subseteq T(q^n)$. Furthermore $\mathcal{L}_G(A)$ is contained in the subgroup of $T(q^n)$ consisting of linear transformations (that is, $\sigma = 1$).

Proof. Let F be the set of linear transformations of V which commute with the action of A on V. Since A acts irreducibly on V, Theorem 15.2 implies that F is a division ring. Clearly $A \subseteq F$. Let F_0 be the smallest division subring of F containing the transformations of A. Then F_0 is clearly a field. We have $F \supseteq F_0$ and V is a vector space over both F and F_0. Now any F_0- subspace of V is an A-subspace so since A acts irreducibly we have $\dim_{F_0} V = 1$. Thus $|F_0| = |V|$ and since $F \supseteq F_0$ we have $F = F_0 = GF(q^n)$. We identify V with the additive group of F. Let $A = \langle h \rangle$ and let $\zeta \in F$ be the element corresponding to h so that if $v \in V$ then $vh = v\zeta$. Since we have field multiplication as well as the action of G on V to contend with, we will use the following notation here to avoid confusion. If $v \in V$, then the image of v under $g \in G$ is v^g. Thus $v^h = v\zeta$.

Now let $g \in G$. Since $A \triangle G$, $g^{-1}hg = h^u$ for some integer u. If s is any integer then $h^s g = gh^{su}$ and hence if $x \in V$ then

$$(x\zeta^s)^g = (x^{h^s})^g = x^{h^s g} = x^{gh^{su}} = (x^g)^{h^{su}} = (x^g)\zeta^{su}.$$

Since $V = GF(q^n)$ it makes sense to set $x = 1$. With $x = 1$, $a = 1^g$ the above yields $\zeta^{su} = a^{-1}(\zeta^s)^g$. Hence we have $(x\zeta^s)^g = (x^g)a^{-1}(\zeta^s)^g$. Define α by $x^\alpha = a^{-1}x^g$. Clearly

α is a linear transformation of V over $GF(q)$. The above equation yields $(x\zeta^s)^\alpha = (x^\alpha)(\zeta^s)^\alpha$. From $F = F_0$ we see that $F = GF(q)(\zeta)$. Hence if $y \in GF(q^n)$ then y is a linear sum over $GF(q)$ of powers of ζ. The above then yields $(xy)^\alpha = x^\alpha y^\alpha$ and α is a field automorphism. Since $x^g = ax^\alpha$ we see that $g \in T(q^n)$. Moreover $g \in \mathcal{L}(h)$ if and only if $\zeta^{su} = \zeta^s$ for all s. This is the case if and only if $\zeta^s = a^{-1}(\zeta^s)^g = (\zeta^s)^\alpha$ for all s or equivalently $\alpha = 1$. Thus the result follows.

We now consider solvable groups. The following two results will be proved simultaneously.

THEOREM 19.9. Let G be a solvable group acting faithfully on vector space V of order q^n. Suppose that G acts transitively on $V^\#$. Then either we can identify V with the additive group of $GF(q^n)$ in such a way that $G \subseteq T(q^n)$ or $q^n = 3^2, 5^2, 7^2, 11^2, 23^2$ or 3^4.

PROPOSITION 19.10. Let G be a solvable group acting faithfully on vector space V of order q^n. Suppose that G

acts regularly on $V^{\#}$. Then either we can identify V with the additive group of $GF(q^n)$ in such a way that $G \subseteq T(q^n)$ or $q^n = 5^2, 7^2, 11^2$ or 23^2. Moreover if $q \neq 2$, then G has a normal subgroup of index 2 unless $q^n = 5^2$ or 11^2. In the latter two cases $G \cong SL(2,3) \times J$ where $|J| = 1$ or 5.

Proof. Let $F = \text{Fit}\, G$ and let F_p denote the Sylow p-subgroup of F. Since $F_p \triangle G$, F_p acts 1/2-transitively on $V^{\#}$ and Theorem 19.6 applies. In particular for $p > 2$, F_p is cyclic and acts semiregularly. There are several possibilities for F_2.

Step 1. G acts irreducibly on V. Let H be a normal cyclic subgroup of G. Then H acts semiregularly. If $\mathcal{C}_G(H)$ is nonabelian, then $|H| \leq q^r - 1$ where $r = [n/2]$. Furthermore if $\mathcal{C}_G(H)$ is nonabelian and $n = 2$ then H consists of scalar matrices and hence $H \subseteq \mathfrak{Z}(G)$.

Since G acts transitively on $V^{\#}$, it certainly acts irreducibly. If H is not semiregular, then H has a subgroup J of order p with $\mathcal{C}_V(J) \neq \langle 0 \rangle$. Since $H \triangle G$ and H is cyclic it follows that $J \triangle G$ and hence $\mathcal{C}_V(J)$ is a proper G-invariant subspace, a contradiction. In particular this implies that $|H|$ is prime to q.

Suppose H acts irreducibly. By the previous proposition, $\mathcal{L}(H)$ is cyclic. Hence if $\mathcal{L}(H)$ is nonabelian then H acts reducibly. By Maschke's theorem we can write $V = V_1 + V_2$ where each V_i is a proper H-invariant subspac[e]. Set $|V_1| = q^r$ and assume that $|V_1| \leq |V_2|$ so that $r \leq [n/[2]]$. Since H acts semiregularly, $|H| \leq |V_1^{\#}| \leq q^r - 1$. Suppose now that $n = 2$ so that $|V_1| = |V_2| = q$. Hence with respect to a suitable basis H consists of diagonal matrices. Suppose $\begin{bmatrix} a & 0 \\ 0 & b \end{bmatrix} = h \in H$. If $a \neq b$ then we see easily that $\mathcal{L}(h)$ consists of diagonal matrices and is therefore abelian. Since this is not the case, H consists of scalar matrices.

<u>Step 2</u>. Let F_2 be cyclic, dihedral, semidihedral or quaternion of order ≥ 16. Then $G \subseteq T(q^n)$.

If F_2 is cyclic, set $A = F$. Then A is a normal cyclic self centralizing subgroup of G by Fitting's theorem. In the other three cases F_2 has a characteristic cyclic subgroup of index 2 and hence F has a characteristic cyclic subgroup A of index 2. Clearly $A \triangle G$ and $\mathcal{C}_F(A) = A$. Let $D = \mathcal{C}_G(A)$ and consider the action of D on F. Clearly D centralizes F_p for all $p > 2$. Now $\operatorname{Aut} F_2$ is a 2-group so $D/\mathcal{C}_D(F)$ is a 2-group. Since $\mathcal{C}_D(F) \subseteq F$, F_p is a Sylow p-subgroup of D for all $p > 2$ and hence D has a normal central 2-complement. This implies that D is a normal nilpotent subgroup of G so $D \subseteq F$ and hence $D = A$. Thus in all cases A is self centralizing.

We show that A acts irreducibly. If not then by the above $|A| < q^{n/2}$. Also $|\operatorname{Aut} A| < |A|$ and G/A is contained isomorphically in $\operatorname{Aut} A$. This yields $|G| < q^{n/2}(q^{n/2} - 1) < q^n - 1$ and so certainly G cannot act transitively on $V^{\#}$, a contradiction. Thus A is irreducible and $G \subseteq T(q^n)$ by Proposition 19.8.

<u>Step 3</u>. Let $F_2 \cong T_0(q)$ with $q = 2^m + 1$. Then $q = 5$ and $|V| = 5^2$.

Set $H = F_2'$. Since $\mathcal{C}(H) \supseteq F_2$ is nonabelian, the results of Step 1 apply. Moreover $n = 2$ here so H consists of scalar matrices. Now $q - 1 = 2^m$ and $|H| \mid (q-1)$ so $H = \langle 1 \rangle$. Assume $q \neq 5$. Then by Proposition 19.7, $\operatorname{Aut} F_2$

is a 2-group. Since $F = F_2$ and $G/\mathcal{L}_G(F_2) \subseteq \text{Aut } F_2$ we see that G is a 2-group. Hence $G = F_2 = T_0(q)$ so that $|G| = 4(q-1)$. Since G is not semiregular and $|G| < 2(q^2-1)$, G cannot act transitively. Thus only $q = 5$ occurs here.

Step 4. If F_2 is quaternion of order 8, then $|V| = 3^2, 5^2, 7^2, 11^2$ or 23^2.

Let $H = \mathcal{L}_G(F_2)$ so that $H \triangle G$. Then H acts 1/2-transitively on $V^{\#}$. Suppose H acts irreducibly on V. Then by Theorem 15.2, the set D of linear transformations of V which commute with all elements of H is a division ring. Since finite division rings are fields, D is commutativ a contradiction since F_2 is a nonabelian group commuting with H. Thus H is not irreducible. By Proposition 19.1 H acts semiregularly and hence $q \nmid |H|$. As in the argument of Step 1 this yields $|H| \leq q^r - 1$ with $r = [n/2]$. Since $|\text{Aut } F_2| = 24$ we have $[G:H] \leq 24$ and hence $|G| \leq 24(q^r-1)$. Now G acts transitively on $V^{\#}$ so $|G| \geq q^n - 1$ and hence $24(q^r-1) \geq (q^n-1)$ and $24 > q^{n-r}$.

We show now that $n = 2$. Note since $\mathfrak{Z}(F_2) \triangle G$ we have $q \neq 2$ by Step 1. Suppose first that n is even and

$n \geq 4$. Then $r = n/2$ and $24 > q^{n/2}$. This yields $q = 3$, $n = 4$ which we consider later. Now let n be odd so that $r = (n-1)/2$. Then $24 > q^{(n+1)/2}$ so $q = 3$, $n = 3$. Now suppose $q = 3$, $n = 3$ or 4. If V_1 is an irreducible H-subspace of V of order q^s with $s \leq [n/2]$ then $|H| \mid (q^s - 1)$. Since $s = 1$ or 2 we see that $|H|$ divides $3-1 = 2$ or $3^2 - 1 = 8$. This implies that H is a normal 2-subgroup of G so $H \subseteq F_2$ and hence $|H| = 2$. Thus $(3^n - 1) \mid |G|$ and $|G| \mid 48$, a contradiction for $n \geq 3$. Thus $n = 2$.

Let $K = F_2$, so that $K \subseteq \mathfrak{Z}(G)$. Since $\mathcal{L}(F) = \mathfrak{Z}(F)$ we see that $\mathcal{L}(F_2) = \mathfrak{Z}(F)$ and hence $H = \mathfrak{Z}(G)$ and H consists of scalar matrices. We have $|H| \mid (q-1)$, $[G:H] \mid 24$ and $(q^2 - 1) \mid |G|$. This yields $(q+1) \mid 24$ and since $q \neq 2$ we have $q = 3, 5, 7, 11$ or 23.

Step 5. Completion of the proof.

The only remaining possibility for F_2 in Theorem 19.6 is that $q^n = 3^4$. Thus Theorem 19.9 is proved. Now suppose G acts regularly. Then F_2 must be cyclic or quaternion. If F_2 is cyclic or quaternion of order ≥ 16

then by Step 2, $G \subseteq T(q^n)$. If F_2 is quaternion of order 8 then by Step 4, $|V| = 3^2, 5^2, 7^2, 11^2$ or 23^2. Consider the case $|V| = 3^2$. Since F_2 acts semiregularly and $|F_2| = 8 = |V^{\#}|$ we see that $G = F_2 G_x$ for some $x \in V^{\#}$. Since G acts semiregularly $G_x = \langle 1 \rangle$ and $G = F_2$. Then G has an irreducible normal cyclic subgroup and $G \subseteq T(3^2)$ by Proposition 19.8. This yields the first half of Proposition 19.10.

Now let $q \neq 2$. Since G acts regularly on $V^{\#}$, $|G| = |V^{\#}|$ is even. If the Sylow 2-subgroups of G are cyclic, then by Theorem 12.7 G has a normal 2-complement and hence a normal subgroup of index 2. We suppose now that the Sylow 2-subgroups of G are quaternion and we consider F_2. If F_2 is cyclic or quaternion of order ≥ 16, then as we saw in Step 2, G contains a normal self centralizing cyclic subgroup A. Clearly $2 \mid [G:A]$ and G/A is contained isomorphically in Aut A, an abelian group. Thus G has a normal subgroup of index 2. Finally suppose F_2 is quaternion of order 8. In Step 4 we showed that we must have $n = 2$ and $\mathcal{L}(F_2) = \mathfrak{Z}(G)$ and this group consists of scalar matrices. Also $G/\mathcal{L}(F_2)$ is contained isomorphically in Aut $F_2 \cong \mathrm{Sym}(4)$. If G has no subgroup of index 2, then certainly $G/\mathfrak{C}(F_2)$ is contained isomorphically in Alt(4). Now $|G| = q^2-1$, $|\mathfrak{Z}(G)| \mid (q-1)$ and $[G:\mathfrak{Z}(G)] \mid 12$ so $(q^2-1) \mid 12(q-1)$ and $(q+1) \mid 12$. Since $q \neq 2$ this yields $q = 3, 5$ or 11. As we showed above, if $q = 3$ then $G = F_2$. Thus only $q^2 = 5^2$ or 11^2 are exceptions.

Let $q^2 = 5^2$ so that $|G| = 5^2 - 1 = 24$. Then F_2 is a normal subgroup of index 3 and $G = F_2K$ where $|K| = 3$. Since $3 \nmid (q-1)$, K does not consist of scalar matrices and hence K does not centralize F_2. This yields $G \cong SL(2, 3)$. Now let $q^2 = 11^2$ so that $|G| = 11^2 - 1 = 120$. Let K be a subgroup of order 3 and let J be a subgroup of order 5. Since $3 \nmid (q-1)$ we see that $F_2K \cong SL(2, 3)$. Now $5 \nmid |\mathrm{Aut}\, F_2|$ so J centralizes F_2 and hence $J \subseteq \mathfrak{Z}(G)$. This yields $G \cong SL(2, 3) \times J$ and the proposition is proved.

The main result of this section is

THEOREM 19.11. (Huppert) Let G be a solvable doubly transitive permutation group. Then either we can identify the set being permuted with $GF(q^n)$ in such a way that

$G \subseteq S(q^n)$ or G has degree $3^2, 5^2, 7^2, 11^2, 23^2$ or 3^4.

Proof. Let V be a minimal normal subgroup of G. Since G is solvable V is an elementary abelian q-group for some prime q. Since G is primitive, V is transitive and since V is abelian, V is a regular normal subgroup of G. Thus $G = G_a V$ and by Proposition 4.2, G_a acts transitively on $V^{\#}$. Thus Theorem 19.9 applies. If $|V| = 3^2, 5^2, 7^2, 11^2, 23^2$ or 3^4 then since $|V| = \deg G$ the result follows. Thus we assume that G_a is not exceptional.

We use additive notation in V and let A be the set of points being permuted. For fixed $a \in A$, $aV = A$ and every element of A is written uniquely as av with $v \in V$. Let $ax \in A$ with $x \in V$. If $v \in V$ then since V is additive $(ax)v = a(x+v)$. Now we identify V with the additive group of $GF(q^n)$ in such a way that $G_a \subseteq T(q^n)$. If $g \in G_a$ then as in Proposition 4.2, $(ax)g = ax^g = a(\zeta x^{\sigma})$ with $\zeta \in GF(q^n)$, σ a field automorphism. Since $G = G_a V$ and $(ax)gv = a(\zeta x^{\sigma})v = a(\zeta x^{\sigma} + v)$ the result follows.

20. SHARP TRANSITIVITY

Let G be a permutation group of degree n on set A. We say G is sharply k-transitive if given any two ordered subsets $\{a_1, \ldots, a_k\}$ and $\{b_1, \ldots, b_k\}$ of A of size k, then there exists one and only one $g \in G$ with $a_i g = b_i$ for all i. Obviously G is sharply k-transitive if and only if G is k-transitive and only the identity in G fixes k points.

PROPOSITION 20.1. Let G be a permutation group on set A with $|A| = n$. Suppose that G is sharply k-transitive. If $a \in A$ and $k > 1$, then G_a is sharply $(k-1)$-transitive on $A - \{a\}$. Also $|G| = n(n-1)\ldots(n-k+1)$.

Proof. Certainly G_a is sharply $(k-1)$-transitive on $A-\{a\}$. Now $[G:G_a] = n$. By induction $|G_a| = (n-1)\ldots(n-k+1)$ so the result on $|G|$ follows.

Now sharp 1-transitivity is precisely regularity. Let G be an arbitrary group. Then G permutes its elements by right multiplication. In this representation we see easily that G is a regular permutation group. Hence $k = 1$ imposes no particular structure on the permutation group. In this section we classify those groups with $k = 2$ or 3. The results here are due to Zassenhaus. In the next section we will consider the remaining possibilities for k.

PROPOSITION 20.2. Let G be a nonsolvable group acting on vector space V of order q^n. Suppose G acts regularly on $V^{\#}$. Then $q^n = 11^2$, 29^2 or 59^2 and $G \simeq SL(2,5) \times J$ where J is a cyclic central subgroup of order $1, 7$ or 29.

<u>Proof</u>. Since G acts semiregularly on $V^{\#}$ we see that $L = VG$, the semidirect product of V by G, is a Frobenius group with kernel V and complement G. Thus by Theorem 18.6, G has a subgroup G_0 with $[G:G_0] = 1$ or 2 and $G_0 = W \times J$ with $W \simeq SL(2,5)$ and J a Z-group of order prime to $2, 3$ and 5. Now G acts regularly so $|G| = q^n - 1$ and in particular $q \nmid |G|$ so $q \neq 2, 3, 5$.

Suppose J acted irreducibly. Then by Theorem 15.2,

the set D of linear transformations of V commuting with the action of J would form a division ring. Since finite division rings are fields, D would be commutative. This contradicts the fact that $W \subseteq \mathcal{L}_G(J)$ and W is nonabelian. Thus J acts reducibly. Let V_1 be a nonzero J-invariant subspace of V of minimal order q^r. Then by Maschke's theorem $r \leq [n/2]$. Since J acts semiregularly $|J| \mid (q^r - 1)$ and in fact $|J| \mid (q^r - 1)/2$ since $q \neq 2$ and $|J|$ is odd.

We show now that $n = 2$ by way of contradiction. First $|G| \leq 240|J|$ and $|J| \leq (q^r - 1)/2$ so $|G| \leq 120(q^r - 1)$. Here $r \leq [n/2]$. Since $|G| = q^n - 1$, this yields $(q^n - 1) \leq 120(q^r - 1)$ or $q^n < 120q^r$. Suppose that $n > 2$. If n is even then $r \leq n/2$ and $q^{n/2} < 120$. Since $q > 5$, the only possibility here is $q = 7$, $n = 4$ which we consider later. If n is odd then $r \leq (n-1)/2$ and $q^{(n+1)/2} < 120$. This yields $q = 7$, $n = 3$. Now let $q = 7$, $n = 3$ or 4. Then $r = 1$ or 2 and $|J| \mid (7-1)$ or $|J| \mid (7^2 - 1)$. Since $|J|$ is prime to 2 and 3 this yields $J = \langle 1 \rangle$. Thus $240 \geq |G| \geq 7^3 - 1$, a contradiction and hence we must have $n = 2$.

Now $G \subseteq GL(2, q)$ and hence if F denotes the algebraic closure of $GF(q)$ then $G \subseteq GL(2, F)$, the group of 2×2 nonsingular matrices over F. Let $g \in G - \mathfrak{Z}(G)$. Since the absolutely irreducible representations of $\langle g \rangle$ are linear, it follows by Maschke's theorem that with respect to a suitable basis $g = \begin{bmatrix} a & 0 \\ 0 & b \end{bmatrix}$. Since $g \notin \mathfrak{Z}(G)$, $a \neq b$ and this implies easily that $\mathcal{L}_G(g)$ consists of diagonal matrices and is therefore abelian. Furthermore if $h \in \mathcal{N}_G(\langle g \rangle)$, then $h^2 \in \mathcal{L}_G(g)$. Now $\mathcal{L}_G(J)$ is nonabelian so this implies that $J \subseteq \mathfrak{Z}(G)$ and J consists of scalar matrices.

Clearly $G = H \times J$ where $|H| = 120$ or 240. We show now that $|H| = 120$ so that $H \simeq SL(2, 5)$. If not then H has a normal subgroup H_0 of index 2 with $H_0 \simeq SL(2, 5)$. Set $K = H/\mathfrak{Z}(H_0)$ and $K_0 = H_0/\mathfrak{Z}(H_0)$. Then $|K| = 120$ and $K_0 \simeq Alt(5)$. We have an obvious homomorphism of K into Aut Alt(5) $\simeq$ Sym(5). If this map is not onto then if C denotes the kernel we have $C \cap K_0 = \langle 1 \rangle$ and $K = K_0 \times C$. Certainly this implies that the Sylow 2-subgroups of H have three generators and are thus not quaternion, a contradiction. Thus $K \simeq Sym(5)$. Let L be the complete inverse image in H of the group $\langle (1\ 2\ 3\ 4\ 5) \rangle$ in Sym(5) and let h be an inverse image in H of the permutation (2 3 4 5). Clearly L is cyclic, h normalizes L but h^2 does not centralize L. This contradicts the above. Hence $|H| = 120$.

We have shown that $G = W \times J$ where $W \simeq SL(2,5)$ and J consists of scalar matrices. Since J has odd order, $|J| \mid (q-1)/2$ and hence $|G| \mid 60(q-1)$. Now $|G| = q^2-1$ so $q+1 \mid 60$ and since $q \neq 2,3,5$ we have $q = 11, 19, 29$ or 59. From $(q^2-1) = 120|J|$ we obtain $|J| = 1, 3, 7$ or 29 respectively. Since $3 \nmid |J|$, $q = 19$ cannot occur and the result follows.

This now combines with our previous results to yield

THEOREM 20.3. (Zassenhaus) Let G be a sharply 2-transitive permutation group. Then either we can identify the set of points being permuted with $GF(q^n)$ in such a way that $G \subseteq S(q^n)$ or G has degree $5^2, 7^2, 11^2, 23^2, 29^2$ or 59^2.

Proof. Let G have degree m so $|G| = m(m-1)$. If a and b are distinct points being permuted then $G_{a,b} = \langle 1 \rangle$

and hence G is a Frobenius group. By Proposition 8.4, G has a regular normal elementary abelian group V of order q^n. Also G_a acts regularly on $V^\#$. If G_a is nonsolvable then $q^n = |V| = 11^2, 29^2$ or 59^2 by Proposition 20.3. Note that $|V| = \deg G$ so the result follows here.

Now assume that G_a is solvable and hence G is solvable. By Proposition 19.10 either $q^n = 5^2, 7^2, 11^2$ or 23^2 or $G_a \subseteq T(q^n)$. As in the proof of Theorem 19.11, the latter implies that $G \subseteq S(q^n)$ and the result follows.

We now consider the case $k = 3$. Let q be a prime. We let $L(q^n)$ denote the group of fractional linear transformations $x \to \dfrac{ax+b}{cx+d}$ with $a, b, c, d \in GF(q^n)$ and $ad-bc \neq 0$. Now $L(q^n)$ permutes the set $GF(q^n) \cup \{\infty\}$ where ∞ satisfies the usual arithmetic rules. $L = L(q^n)$ is certainly transitive since $\{x+b\}$ is transitive on $GF(q^n)$ and $1/x$ interchanges 0 and ∞. We see easily that $L_\infty = \{ax+b\}$ and this is a sharply 2-transitive group. Hence $L(q^n)$ is a sharply 3-transitive group of degree $1+q^n$.

Now suppose that $q \neq 2$ and that n is even. Since $q \neq 2$ the multiplicative group of $GF(q^n)$ is a cyclic group of even order and hence has a characteristic subgroup of index 2. The map $x \longrightarrow x^2$ is clearly a homomorphism of $GF(q^n)-\{0\}$ into this subgroup of index 2. If $x^2 = 1$, then $x = \pm 1$ and hence the kernel has order 2 and the image of this homomorphism has index 2 in $GF(q^n)-\{0\}$. Thus the set of squares in $GF(q^n)-\{0\}$ is a characteristic subgroup of index 2. Now since n is even, $GF(q^n)$ has a unique field automorphism σ of order 2. This is given by $x^\sigma = x^{q^r}$ where $r = n/2$. We let $M(q^n)$ denote the set of fractional transformations of the form $x \longrightarrow \frac{ax + b}{cx + d}$

if $ad-bc$ is a nonzero square and $x \longrightarrow \frac{ax^\sigma + b}{cx^\sigma + d}$ if

$ad-bc$ is not a square. Here $a, b, c, d \in GF(q^n)$. It is an easy matter to check that $M(q^n)$ is in fact a group under composition multiplication. Again $M = M(q^n)$ permutes the set $GF(q^n) \cup \{\infty\}$. Clearly M_∞ consists of those semilinear transformations of the form $ax+b$ with a a nonzero square and $ax^\sigma + b$ with a not a square. In particular we can map the ordered set $\{0, 1\}$ to $\{b, a+b\}$ for all choices of $a \neq 0$ and b. Since $|M_\infty| = q^n(q^n - 1)$ this implies that M_∞ is sharply 2-transitive on $GF(q^n)$.

Now $-1/x \in M$ and this interchanges 0 and ∞. Hence M is transitive and since M_∞ is sharply 2-transitive, M is sharply 3-transitive.

The main result of this section is that the above are the only sharply 3-transitive groups.

LEMMA 20.4. Let H be a group and let τ be an automorphism of H of order 2.

i. If $\mathcal{L}_H(\tau) = \langle 1 \rangle$, then H is abelian and for all $h \in H$, $h\tau = h^{-1}$.

ii. Let $|\mathcal{L}_H(\tau)| = 2$ and suppose that H has a subgroup of index 2. Then H has a τ-invariant abelian subgroup $\bar{H}$ of index 2 with $h\tau = h^{-1}$ for all $h \in \bar{H}$.

Proof. Let $g, h \in H$. Then $g^{-1}(g\tau) = h^{-1}(h\tau)$ if and only if $(hg^{-1})\tau = hg^{-1}$. Thus if $T = \{h^{-1}(h\tau) \mid \text{all } h \in H\}$ then $|T| = [H: \mathcal{L}_H(\tau)]$. Let $g \in T$ so that $g = h^{-1}(h\tau)$. Since $\tau^2 = 1$ we have $g\tau = (h^{-1}\tau)(h\tau^2) = (h\tau)^{-1}h = (h^{-1}(h\tau))^{-1} = g^{-1}$. If T is a subgroup of H and if $g_1, g_2 \in T$ then we have $g_2^{-1}g_1^{-1} = (g_1g_2)^{-1} = (g_1g_2)\tau = (g_1\tau)(g_2\tau) = g_1^{-1}g_2^{-1}$ and hence $g_1g_2 = g_2g_1$. Thus T is abelian and for all $g \in T$, $g\tau = g^{-1}$.

Suppose now that $\mathcal{L}_H(\tau) = \langle 1 \rangle$. Then $|T| = |H|$ so $T = H$ is a subgroup of H. The above clearly yields (i). Now let $|\mathcal{L}_H(\tau)| = 2$ so that $|T| = |H|/2$. Let N be a subgroup of H of index 2. Clearly $N \triangleleft H$. We show first that H has a τ-invariant subgroup $\bar{H}$ of index 2. If $N = N\tau$ set $\bar{H} = N$. If $N \neq N\tau$ then since $\tau^2 = 1$, $M = N \cap N\tau$ is a τ-invariant subgroup of H and H/M is abelian of type $(2,2)$. Now τ permutes the three subgroups of H/M of order 2 and hence τ must fix one of these say $\bar{H}/M$. Clearly $\bar{H}$ is a τ-invariant subgroup of H of index 2. Since $H/\bar{H}$ has order 2 we see that τ must act trivially on this quotient. Hence for all $h \in H$, $h \equiv h\tau \mod \bar{H}$. This implies that $\bar{H} \supseteq T$ and hence $T = \bar{H}$ since $|T| = |\bar{H}| = |H|/2$. The result now follows since T is a subgroup of H.

THEOREM 20.5. (Zassenhaus) Let G be a sharply 3-transitive permutation group of degree $1+m$. Then

$m = q^n$ for some prime q and we can identify the set of points being permuted with $GF(q^n) \cup \{\infty\}$ in such a way that $G = L(q^n)$ or $M(q^n)$. Thus we have two groups if n is even and $q \neq 2$ and one group in the remaining cases.

Proof. Denote by ∞ one of the points being permuted. Then G_∞ is a sharply 2-transitive group of degree m. Thus G_∞ has a regular normal subgroup V and a complement $G_{\infty 0}$ where 0 is another point being permuted. Of course V is an elementary abelian q-group for some prime q and hence $m = |V| = q^n$. The group $G_{\infty 0}$ acts faithfully on V and regularly on $V^\#$. Thus Propositions 19.10 and 20.2 apply to $G_{\infty 0}$.

Step 1. $G_{\infty 0}$ contains at most one subgroup of order 3. In particular $G_{\infty 0}$ cannot contain isomorphic copies of $SL(2,3)$ or $SL(2,5)$. Thus we can identify the set of points being permuted by G_∞ with $GF(q^n)$ in such a way that $G_{\infty 0} \subseteq T(q^n)$.

We need only show that $G_{\infty 0}$ contains at most one subgroup of order 3. The remaining contentions then follow from Propositions 19.10 and 20.2. We will use the following two facts freely. First since G is triply transitive, G contains an element which moves three points in any prescribed manner. Second, since G is sharply 3-transitive any two elements of G which agree on their action on three points are identical.

Let u and v be two distinct elements of $G_{\infty 0}$ of order 3. Since these elements fix 0 and ∞ but no other point they have the form $u = (0)(\infty)(1\ 2\ 3)\ldots$ and $v = (0)(\infty)(1\ a\ b)\ldots$ with $a, b \neq 2, 3$ respectively. Choose $g \in G$ with $g = (1)(2\ 3)\ldots$. Then $u^g = (1\ 3\ 2)\ldots$ and hence $u^g = u^{-1}$ since they agree on three points. Certainly g must send the points fixed by u to the points fixed by u^{-1} and hence g permutes the set $\{0, \infty\}$. Since g already has one fixed point, namely 1, we must have $g = (0\ \infty)(1)(2\ 3)\ldots$.

Now choose $h \in G$ with $h = \begin{pmatrix} 1 & 2 & 3 & \ldots \\ 1 & a & b & \ldots \end{pmatrix}$. Then $u^h = v$ since u^h and v agree on three points. Since $v \neq u$ we have $h \neq 1$. Now h must send the points fixed by u to the points fixed by v and hence h permutes the set $\{0, \infty\}$.

Since h already has one fixed point, namely 1, we must have $h = (0\ \infty)(1)\ldots.$ Thus g and h agree on three points and $g = h$. This yields $v = u^h = u^g = u^{-1}$ and the result follows.

Step 2. We assume now that G permutes the set $GF(q^n) \cup \{\infty\}$ and 0 and 1 are the obvious elements of $GF(q^n)$. We choose $g \in G$ with $g = (0\ \infty)(1)\ldots$ and fix this throughout the remainder of the proof. Then g has order 2 and g normalizes $H = G_{\infty 0}$. If $h \in G_{\infty 0}$ then $(1)hg = (1)h^g$ and hence $|\mathcal{L}_H(g)| \leq 2$.

Given $g = (0\ \infty)(1)\ldots$ we have $g^2 = (0)(\infty)(1)\ldots$ and hence $g^2 = 1$. Since g interchanges 0 and ∞ it is obvious that g normalizes $H = G_{\infty 0}$. If $h \in G_{\infty 0}$ then since $1g = g$ we have $1h^g = 1(g^{-1}hg) = (1h)g$. Now $G_{\infty 0}$ acts regularly on $GF(q^n)^{\#} = GF(q^n) - \{0\}$ and since g fixes at most two points we have $|\mathcal{L}_H(g)| \leq 2$.

Step 3. If $q = 2$, then $G = L(q^n)$.

Since $q = 2$, $|G_{\infty 0}| = q^n - 1$ is odd and since $|\mathcal{L}_H(g)| \leq 2$ we have $\mathcal{L}_H(g) = \langle 1 \rangle$. By Lemma 20.4 H is abelian and $h^g = h^{-1}$ for all $h \in H$. Since G_∞ is a Frobenius group and H is a Frobenius complement we see that H is cyclic. This implies easily by Proposition 19.8 that the elements of $G_{\infty 0}$ are all of the form $\begin{pmatrix} x \\ ax \end{pmatrix}$ with $a \in GF(q^n)$, $a \neq 0$ and hence G_∞ consists of elements of the form $\begin{pmatrix} x \\ ax+b \end{pmatrix}$. Furthermore since G_∞ is doubly transitive, it contains all linear transformations of this type.

Suppose $g = \begin{pmatrix} x \\ f(x) \end{pmatrix}$. We know that $f(0) = \infty$, $f(\infty) = 0$ and $f(1) = 1$. Let $a \in GF(q^n)$, $a \neq 0$. From

$$\begin{pmatrix} x \\ f(x) \end{pmatrix} \begin{pmatrix} x \\ a^{-1}x \end{pmatrix} = \begin{pmatrix} x \\ ax \end{pmatrix} \begin{pmatrix} x \\ f(x) \end{pmatrix}$$

applied to $x = 1$ we obtain $a^{-1} = f(a)$. Thus for all x, $f(x) = 1/x$.

By Proposition 3.7, $G = G_\infty \cup G_\infty g G_\infty$. Since

$$\begin{pmatrix} x \\ ax + b \end{pmatrix} \begin{pmatrix} x \\ 1/x \end{pmatrix} \begin{pmatrix} x \\ cx + d \end{pmatrix} = \begin{pmatrix} x \\ (a_1x+b_1)/(c_1x+d_1) \end{pmatrix}$$

with $a_1 = ad$, $b_1 = bd+c$, $c_1 = a$, $d_1 = b$ and with $a_1d_1 - b_1c_1 = -ac \neq 0$, the result follows.

<u>Step 4.</u> For the remainder of the proof we assume that $q \neq 2$. Then H has a cyclic subgroup $\bar{H}$ of index 2 with $h^g = h^{-1}$ for all $h \in \bar{H}$. Moreover we have one of the following two possibilities.

i. G_∞ consists of all linear transformations of the type $\begin{pmatrix} x \\ ax+b \end{pmatrix}$ with $a, b \in GF(q^n)$, $a \neq 0$.

ii. G_∞ consists of all transformations of the form $\begin{pmatrix} x \\ ax+b \end{pmatrix}$ with $a \neq 0$ a square in $GF(q^n)$ and of the form $\begin{pmatrix} x \\ ax^\sigma+b \end{pmatrix}$ with a a nonsquare in $GF(q^n)$ and σ a field automorphism of order 2.

By Step 1, H is a solvable group which acts regularly on $V^\#$. Moreover H does not contain an isomorphic copy of $SL(2,3)$. By Proposition 19.10, since $|H| = q^2-1$ is even, H has a normal subgroup of index 2. Now g acts on H and since $o(g) = 2$, $2 \mid |H|$ we must have $|\mathcal{L}_H(g)| \geq 2$. On the other hand by Step 2, $|\mathcal{L}_H(g)| \leq 2$ so $|\mathcal{L}_H(g)| = 2$. By

Lemma 20.4, H has a normal abelian subgroup $\bar{H}$ of index 2 which is normalized by g. Moreover for all $h \in \bar{H}$, $h^g = h^{-1}$. Since $\bar{H}$ is a Frobenius complement it is therefore cyclic.

Now $\bar{H}$ acts semiregularly and $|\bar{H}| = (q^n - 1)/2$ so certainly $\bar{H}$ acts irreducibly on V. Therefore Proposition 19.8 applies. If H is abelian then clearly G_∞ satisfies (i). Moreover $\bar{H}$ is the set of all transformations of the form $\begin{pmatrix} x \\ ax \end{pmatrix}$ with a a nonzero square in $GF(q^n)$. Now let H be nonabelian. Then H consists of transformations of the form $\begin{pmatrix} x \\ ax \end{pmatrix}$ and $\begin{pmatrix} x \\ ax^\sigma \end{pmatrix}$ where σ is a field automorphism of order 2. Since $\bar{H}$ is a subgroup of index 2 of the group of all $\begin{pmatrix} x \\ ax \end{pmatrix}$ we see that $\bar{H}$ is the set of all $\begin{pmatrix} x \\ ax \end{pmatrix}$ with a a nonzero square. Let $h = \begin{pmatrix} x \\ ax^\sigma \end{pmatrix} \in H$. If a is a square then $k = \begin{pmatrix} x \\ ax \end{pmatrix} \in H$ and hence $hk^{-1} = \begin{pmatrix} x \\ x^\sigma \end{pmatrix} \in H$. However this element fixes all $x \in V$ in the fixed field of σ and this contradicts the fact that H acts semiregularly on $V^\#$. Thus we see that if $h \in H$ with

$h = \begin{pmatrix} x \\ ax^{\sigma} \end{pmatrix}$, then a is a nonsquare. By order considerations H contains all such transformations and we see easily that G_{∞} satisfies (ii).

<u>Step 5</u>. $G = G_{\infty} \cup G_{\infty} gV$ and $g = \begin{pmatrix} x \\ 1/x \end{pmatrix}$.

By Proposition 3.7, $G = G_{\infty} \cup G_{\infty} g G_{\infty}$. Now $G_{\infty} = G_{\infty 0} V$ and g normalizes $G_{\infty 0}$ so

$$G_{\infty} g G_{\infty} = G_{\infty} g G_{\infty 0} V = G_{\infty} G_{\infty 0} g V = G_{\infty} g V$$

and the first result follows.

Let $g = \begin{pmatrix} x \\ f(x) \end{pmatrix}$. We know that $f(0) = \infty$, $f(\infty) = 0$ and $f(1) = 1$. Now g centralizes some element of order 2 in H. By Theorem 18.1, H has a unique element of order 2, namely $\begin{pmatrix} x \\ -x \end{pmatrix}$ so

$$\begin{pmatrix} x \\ -x \end{pmatrix}\begin{pmatrix} x \\ f(x) \end{pmatrix} = \begin{pmatrix} x \\ f(x) \end{pmatrix}\begin{pmatrix} x \\ -x \end{pmatrix}$$

and $f(-x) = -f(x)$. Suppose a is a square in $GF(q^n)$. Then

$\begin{pmatrix} x \\ ax \end{pmatrix} \in \bar{H}$ and

$$\begin{pmatrix} x \\ ax \end{pmatrix} \begin{pmatrix} x \\ f(x) \end{pmatrix} = \begin{pmatrix} x \\ f(x) \end{pmatrix} \begin{pmatrix} x \\ a^{-1}x \end{pmatrix}$$

and hence $f(ax) = a^{-1}f(x)$. Evaluating this at $x = 1$ yields $f(a) = a^{-1}$ and thus $f(ax) = f(a)f(x)$. We repeat again that these results hold so far only if a is a nonzero square.

Since f permutes the nonzero squares of $GF(q^n)$ it therefore permutes the nonsquares. This shows that for all $x \in GF(q^n)^{\#}$, $f(x)x^{-1}$ is a square.

Let a be a nonzero square in $GF(q^n)$. Then

$$\begin{pmatrix} x \\ f(x) \end{pmatrix} \begin{pmatrix} x \\ x+a \end{pmatrix} \begin{pmatrix} x \\ f(x) \end{pmatrix} = \begin{pmatrix} x \\ f(f(x)+a) \end{pmatrix}$$

belongs to $G_\infty \cup G_\infty gV$. Since $a \neq 0$ we see that this permutation does not fix the point ∞ and hence it belongs to $G_\infty gV$. Now V consists of the translations, that is the permutations of the form $\begin{pmatrix} x \\ x+c \end{pmatrix}$ and hence we see easily that

$$f(f(x) + a) = f(a'x + b) + c$$

or

$$= f(a'x^{\sigma} + b) + c.$$

We now solve for a', b and c. First evaluating at ∞ yields clearly $f(a) = c$. Now evaluating at 0 yields $0 = f(\infty + a) = f(b) + c = f(b) + f(a)$. Since $g^2 = 1$ we have $b = f(f(b)) = f(-f(a)) = -f(f(a)) = -a$. Thus

$$f(f(x) + a) = f(a'x - a) + f(a)$$

or

$$= f(a'x^{\sigma} - a) + f(a).$$

We show now that the latter possibility cannot occur. Define $y \in GF(q^n)$ by $a'y^{\sigma} = a$. If the second possibility occurs, then evaluating at y yields immediately $f(f(y) + a) = f(0) + f(a) = \infty + f(a) = \infty$ and thus $f(y) + a = 0$. Hence $y = f(f(y)) = f(-a) = -f(a) = -a^{-1}$ and $a' = -aa^{\sigma}$. Since a is a square so is a^{σ}. Also if this situation occurs then n is even and $4 \mid (q^n - 1)$. This implies that -1 is a square in $GF(q^n)$ and hence a' is a square, a contradiction. Thus

$$f(f(x) + a) = f(a'x - a) + f(a).$$

Define $y \in GF(q^n)$ by $a'y = a$. Then evaluating at y yields as above $y = -a^{-1}$ and hence $a' = -a^2$. Therefore

$$f(f(x) + a) = f(-a^2 x - a) + f(a).$$

At $x = -1$ since $f(-1) = -f(1) = -1$ we obtain easily $f(a-1) = f(a^2 - a) + f(a) = f(a)f(a-1) + f(a)$ where the latter follows from $a^2 - a = a(a-1)$ and the fact that a is a square. Thus $f(a-1) = f(a)/(1-f(a)) = a^{-1}/(1-a^{-1}) = (a-1)^{-1}$.

We show now that $f(x) = 1/x$ for all x. We can clearly assume that $x \neq 0, \infty, 1, -1$. Now

$$x = ((x-1)/2)^2 \left\{((x+1)/(x-1))^2 - 1\right\}.$$

Since $((x-1)/2)^2$ and $((x+1)/(x-1))^2$ are squares we have

$$\begin{aligned} f(x) &= ((x-1)/2)^{-2} f(((x+1)/(x-1))^2 - 1) \\ &= ((x-1)/2)^{-2} \left\{((x-1)/(x-1))^2 - 1\right\}^{-1} = 1/x \end{aligned}$$

and the result follows.

<u>Step 6.</u> $G = L(q^n)$ or $M(q^n)$.

We have $G = G_\infty \cup V g G_\infty$ and V consists of translations. Let γ denote a field automorphism of order

1 or 2. Then

$$\begin{pmatrix} x \\ x+a \end{pmatrix}\begin{pmatrix} x \\ 1/x \end{pmatrix}\begin{pmatrix} x \\ bx^{\tau}+c \end{pmatrix} = \begin{pmatrix} x \\ (a'x^{\tau}+b')/(c'x^{\tau}+d') \end{pmatrix}$$

where $a' = c$, $b' = a^{\tau}c + b$, $c' = 1$, $d' = a^{\tau}$ and with $a'd' - b'c' = -b \neq 0$. Thus if G_{∞} is the type (i) group of Step 4, then $G = L(q^n)$. If G_{∞} is the type (ii) group then n is even, $4 \mid (q^n - 1)$ and hence -1 is a square in $GF(q^n)$. Thus we see that $a'd' - b'c'$ is a square if and only if b is and therefore $G = M(q^n)$. This completes the proof of the theorem.

Again let τ be a field automorphism and consider the function $x \to \dfrac{ax^{\tau} + b}{cx^{\tau} + d}$. Certainly a, b, c and d are not uniquely determined. However it is easy to see that the only other values are all of the form $a' = \lambda a$, $b' = \lambda b$, $c' = \lambda c$, $d' = \lambda d$ where $\lambda \in GF(q^n)^{\#}$. Then $a'd' - b'c' = \lambda^2(ad - bc)$ so that this determinant function is unique only up to a square factor. In any case it makes sense to talk about its parity, that is whether it is a square or not. It is eay to see that the set of functions in $L(q^n)$ and

$M(q^n)$ whose determinant is a square is a normal subgroup of index 1 or 2. It has index 2 if $q \neq 2$ and index 1 if $q = 2$, since every element is a square in $GF(2^n)$. Thus for $q \neq 2$, $L(q^n)$ and $M(q^n)$ are not simple groups. We consider the case $q = 2$ below.

LEMMA 20.6. Let H be a Frobenius group with kernel K. Then K is characteristic in H. Furthermore if $N \triangle H$ then either $N \geq K$ or $K \supsetneq N$.

Proof. We have seen in Corollary 17.5 that $K = \text{Fit } H$. Thus K is characteristic in H. Let $N \triangle H$ and suppose that $K \not\supseteq N$ and $N \not\supseteq K$. Set $M = K \cap N$ so that $M \triangle H$ and $K > M$, $N > M$. By Proposition 17.3 $\bar{H} = H/M$ is a Frobenius group with kernel $\bar{K} = K/M$. Now $\bar{N} \cap \bar{K} = \langle 1 \rangle$ so $\bar{N}$ centralizes $\bar{K}$ and $\bar{N} \neq \langle 1 \rangle$. This contradicts Proposition 17.2 and the result follows.

THEOREM 20.7. (Suzuki) Let G be a doubly transitive permutation group of degree $1 + m$ with m even. Suppose further that the only element of G fixing three points is the identity. Then either G is a Frobenius group of G is simple

Proof. We assume that G is not a Frobenius group and prove that it is simple. Let G permute the set A and let $N \triangle G$ with $N \neq \langle 1 \rangle$. Suppose first that N is regular. Then for $a \in A$, the action of G_a on N and on A are the same. In particular if $g \in G_a^{\#}$ then $|\mathcal{L}_N(g)| \leq 2$. Now $|N| = 1+m$ is odd so this yields $\mathcal{L}_N(g) = \langle 1 \rangle$. Thus G_a acts semiregularly on $N^{\#}$ and G is a Frobenius group, a contradiction. Now suppose that N is a Frobenius group in this action with kernel K. Then by the above lemma, K is characteristic in N and hence normal in G. Thus K is a regular normal subgroup of G, a contradiction.

We have shown above that N is neither regular nor a Frobenius group. Since G is doubly transitive, it is primitive and hence N is transitive. We consider $N_a = (N \cap G_a) \triangle G_a$. Since N is not regular $N_a \neq \langle 1 \rangle$. Now G_a is transitive on $A - \{a\}$ and by assumption no nonidentity element of G_a can fix two points of $A - \{a\}$. Furthermore since G is not a Frobenius group, G_a is not semiregular on $A-\{a\}$. Hence G_a is a Frobenius group on $A-\{a\}$ and let K be its kernel. Now $N_a \triangle G_a$ so by the previous lemma either $K \supseteq N_a$ or $N_a \supseteq K$. If $K \supseteq N_a$, then N_a acts semiregularly on $A-\{a\}$ and hence N is a Frobenius group, a contradiction. Thus $N_a \supseteq K$. Since K is transitive on $A-\{a\}$, the same is true for N_a and hence N is doubly transitive.

We have $[N:N_a] = 1+m$ and $m \mid |N_a|$ so $m(m+1) \mid |N|$. On the other hand $|G_a| \mid m(m-1)$ so $|G| \mid (m+1)m(m-1)$. This yields $|G/N| \mid (m-1)$ and hence G/N is a group of odd order.

Let θ be the character of the permutation representation, that is $\theta(g)$ is the number of points fixed by g. By assumption if $g \neq 1$ then $\theta(g) \leq 2$. Suppose $\theta(g) = 1$. Then for some point a, $g \in G_a$. Let G_a be as above. Since g fixes no point of $A-\{a\}$ we have $g \in K \subseteq N_a \subseteq N$ and hence $g \in N$. Now let $\theta(g) = 0$. Then g is the product of cycles of length > 1. Since $1+m$ is odd at least one of these cycles has odd length. Let r be the minimal length of all these cycles of odd length so that $r \geq 3$. Then g^r fixes $r \geq 3$ points and $g^r = 1$. This shows that all cycles of g have length r and hence $r \mid (m+1)$. Since r is odd, this yields $(r, m-1) = 1$ and hence since $|G/N| \mid (m-1)$ we have $g \in N$. We have therefore shown that if $g \in G-N$ then $\theta(g) = 2$.

We have clearly $\sum_{g \in G-N} \theta(g)^2 = 4(|G|-|N|)$. On the other hand since both G and N are doubly transitive Proposition 3.9 yields

$$\sum_{g \in G-N} \theta(g)^2 = \sum_{g \in G} \theta(g)^2 - \sum_{g \in N} \theta(g)^2$$
$$= 2|G| - 2|N|.$$

Therefore $|N| = |G|$, $G = N$ and G is simple.

COROLLARY 20.8. If $q = 2$, $n \geq 2$ then $L(q^n)$ is simple.

Proof. We have seen that $G = L(q^n)$ is sharply 3-transitive of degree $1+q^n$ and hence G satisfies the hypothesis of the previous theorem. If $n \geq 2$ then at least 5 points are being permuted and hence we can find $g \in G$ with $g = \begin{pmatrix} 1 & 2 & 3 & \ldots \\ 1 & 2 & 4 & \ldots \end{pmatrix}$. Then g fixes two points and $g \neq 1$. This shows that G is not a Frobenius group and hence G

is simple.

21. THE MATHIEU GROUPS

In this section we conclude our investigation of the sharply k-transitive groups by considering the possibility $k \geq 4$.

PROPOSITION 21.1. Sym(n) is sharply n-transitive and sharply (n-1)-transitive of degree n. If $n \geq 3$, then Alt(n) is sharply (n-2)-transitive of degree n.

Proof. By Proposition 3.5 Sym(n) and Alt(n) have the appropriate transitivity properties. If $g \in$ Sym(n) fixes n-1 points then clearly $g = 1$. If $g \in$ Sym(n) fixes n-2 points then either $g = 1$ or g is a transposition. Since Alt(n) contains no transpositions the result follows.

We will consider the above examples as being trivial. Before we consider the nontrivial groups we first obtain a few preliminary results.

PROPOSITION 21.2. Let G be a t-transitive group of degree n. Let H be the subgroup fixing t points and let P be a Sylow p-subgroup of H. Suppose P fixes $w \geq t$ points. Then $\mathcal{N}_G(P)$ is t-transitive on the w points fixed by P.

Proof. We assume that H is the subgroup fixing the points $a_1, a_2, \ldots, a_t$ and show that if P fixes points $b_1, b_2, \ldots, b_t$ then there exists $g \in \mathcal{N}_G(P)$ with $a_i g = b_i$. Since G is t-transitive there exists $x \in G$ with $a_i x = b_i$. Now P fixes $b_1, b_2, \ldots, b_t$ so xPx^{-1} fixes $a_1, a_2, \ldots, a_t$ and hence xPx^{-1} is also a Sylow p-subgroup of H. By Sylow's theorem there exists $y \in H$ with $y(xPx^{-1})y^{-1} = P$. Set $g = yx$. Then $g \in \mathcal{N}_G(P)$ and we have $a_i g = a_i yx = a_i x = b_i$ so the result follows.

LEMMA 21.3. Suppose G is sharply k-transitive of degree n. Then we cannot have $k = 4$, $n = 10$ or $k = 6$, $n = 13$.

Proof. The proofs of the two cases are essentially

the same. Suppose first that $k = 4$, $n = 10$. Then $|G| = 10 \cdot 9 \cdot 8 \cdot 7$. If $x \in G$ has order 7 then $\langle x \rangle$ is a Sylow 7-subgroup of G and x is a 7-cycle, say $x = (1\ 2\ 3\ 4\ 5\ 6\ 7)$. Now G is 3-transitive and $\langle x \rangle$ is a Sylow 7-subgroup of the subgroup of G fixing $\{8, 9, 10\}$. Thus by Proposition 21.2, $\mathcal{N}(\langle x \rangle)$ acts 3-transitively on $\{8, 9, 10\}$ and thus the restriction map yields a homomorphism of $\mathcal{N}(\langle x \rangle)$ onto Sym $\{8, 9, 10\}$. Since $\mathcal{L}(x) \triangle \mathcal{N}(\langle x \rangle)$, the image of $\mathcal{L}(x)$ must be a normal subgroup and the image cannot be $\langle 1 \rangle$ since $\mathcal{N}(\langle x \rangle)/\mathcal{L}(x)$ is abelian. Hence $3 \,\|\, |\mathcal{L}(x)|$ and we can choose $y \in \mathcal{L}(x)$ with $o(y) = 3$. Then $o(xy) = 21$ and xy must therefore consist of a 7-cycle and a 3-cycle. Thus $(xy)^7 \neq 1$ but $(xy)^7$ fixes 7 points, a contradiction since G is sharply 4-transitive.

Now let $k = 6$, $n = 13$, so that $|G| = 13 \cdot 12 \cdot 11 \cdot 10 \cdot 9 \cdot 8$. If $x \in G$ has order 5 then $\langle x \rangle$ is a Sylow 5-subgroup of G. Also x is the product of two 5-cycles since it cannot fix eight points and hence say $x = (1\ 2\ 3\ 4\ 5)(6\ 7\ 8\ 9\ 10)$. Since G is 3-transitive, the same argument as above shows that there exists $y \in \mathcal{L}(x)$ with $o(y) = 3$. The element xy has order 15 and since it cannot contain a 15-cycle, it must consist of 3-cycles and 5-cycles. Also $(xy)^6 = x$ so xy must have two 5-cycles and one 3-cycle. Then $(xy)^5 \neq 1$ but this element fixes ten points, a contradiction and the lemma is proved.

It is convenient now to point out a few simple facts about the group Sym(4).

LEMMA 21.4. Sym(4) contains precisely three elements of order 2 which act without fixed points. These elements along with the identity form a regular normal subgroup. In particular every element of order 2 not in this subgroup has two fixed points.

Proof. Let $x \in \mathrm{Sym}(4)$ have order 2 and no fixed point. Suppose $1x = a \in \{2, 3, 4\}$. If b, c are the remaining two elements then clearly $x = (1\ a)(b\ c)$. Since x is uniquely determined by a there are at most three such elements x. It is easy to check that $\{1, (1\ 2)(3\ 4), (1\ 3)(2\ 4), (1\ 4)(2\ 3)\}$ is a regular subgroup of Sym(4). It is then clearly normal. All other elements of order 2 in Sym(4) are transpositions and have two fixed points.

In the following result the examples of Proposition 21.1 are considered trivial.

THEOREM 21.5. (Jordan) Let G be a nontrivial sharply k-transitive group of degree n. If $k \geq 4$, then we have either $k = 4$, $n = 11$ or $k = 5$, $n = 12$.

Proof. We proceed in a series of steps.

Step 1. Let $k = 4$. Then we must have $n \geq 8$ and all elements of G of order 2 are conjugate in G.

We must of course have $n \geq 4$ and $|G| = n(n-1)(n-2)(n-3)$. If $n = 4$ or 5 then $|G| = n!$ so $G = \mathrm{Sym}(n)$, a contradiction. If $n = 6$ then $|G| = n!/2$ so $G = \mathrm{Alt}(n)$, again a contradiction. Now let $n = 7$. Then $|G| = 7!/6$ so $[\mathrm{Sym}(7):G] = 6$. Since $\mathrm{Sym}(7)$ transitively permutes the right cosets of G we have a homomorphism of $\mathrm{Sym}(7)$ into a transitive subgroup of $\mathrm{Sym}(6)$. This is a contradiction by order considerations and the fact that $\mathrm{Alt}(7)$ is the only proper normal subgroup of Sym(7). Thus $n \geq 8$.

Let $x, y \in G$ both have order 2. Since they fix at most three points and $n \geq 8$ we must have $x = (1\ 2)(3\ 4)\ldots$ and $y = (a\ b)(c\ d)\ldots$, that is at least two transpositions must occur in each. Choose $g \in G$ with $g = \begin{pmatrix} 1 & 2 & 3 & 4 & \ldots \\ a & b & c & d & \ldots \end{pmatrix}$ so that $x^g = (a\ b)(c\ d)\ldots$. Since x^g and y agree on four points they are equal and the fact follows.

Step 2. If $k = 4$, then $n = 11$.

Let $x = (1)(2)(3\ 4)\ldots$, $y = (1\ 2)(3)(4)\ldots$ belong to G. Then x^2 and y^2 fix four points so $x^2 = y^2 = 1$. Also xy and yx agree on points $\{1, 2, 3, 4\}$ so that $xy = yx$. Set $z = xy$ so that $z = (1\ 2)(3\ 4)\ldots$. Now x has at most three fixed points. If it has a third fixed point we denote this by 7. In the following whenever we write (7) we will always allow for the possibility that this term does not occur. Since y centralizes x, it must permute the set of fixed points of x. Thus y fixes 7. Hence $x = (1)(2)(3\ 4)(7)\ldots$, $y = (1\ 2)(3)(4)(7)\ldots$ and $z = xy = (1\ 2)(3\ 4)(7)\ldots$. Now z is conjugate to x so z has two or three fixed points and in fact two fixed elements other than 7. Say z fixes 5 and 6. The elements x and y centralize z so they must permute the fixed points of z. Since we have already accounted for all fixed points of x and y, each must interchange 5 and 6. Thus we have

$$x = (1)(2)(3\ 4)(5\ 6)(7)\ldots$$

$$y = (1\ 2)(3)(4)(5\ 6)(7)\ldots$$

$$z = (1\ 2)(3\ 4)(5)(6)(7)\ldots$$

and $\langle x, y, z \rangle = H$ is an elementary abelian group of order 4.

Suppose $w \in G$ centralizes H. Then w must fix the common fixed point 7. Further w permutes the fixed points of x, of y and of z and hence

$$w = (1\ 2)^{\alpha}(3\ 4)^{\beta}(5\ 6)^{\gamma}(7)\ldots$$

with $\alpha, \beta, \gamma = 0, 1$. If $w \neq 1$ then w fixes at most three points so at least two of α, β, γ are equal to 1. This yields clearly $w = x, y, z$ or $w = (1\ 2)(3\ 4)(5\ 6)(7)\ldots$. In the latter case $xw \neq 1$ fixes four points, a contradiction, and hence H is self centralizing. Let $N = \mathcal{N}_G(H)$. Since $|\text{Aut } H| = 6$ we have $|N| \leq 24$.

Now $\{1,2,3,4,5,6,7\}$ is a union of orbits of H which contains the fixed points of all elements of $H^{\#}$. Thus H acts regularly on all further orbits. There is at least one more orbit since $n \geq 8$. Let $\{a,b,c,d\}$ be such an orbit. Let W be the set of elements of G which permute this set. Since G is sharply 4-transitive, $W \simeq \mathrm{Sym}(4)$ and H is a regular subgroup of W. By the previous lemma $H \triangle W$ and hence since $|N| \leq 24$, $|W| = 24$ we have $N = W \simeq \mathrm{Sym}(4)$. Let g be a fixed element of N-H of order 2. By the previous lemma g has two fixed points in $\{a,b,c,d\}$. If H has two such orbits, then g fixes two points in each and $g \neq 1$ has four fixed points, a contradiction. Thus there are precisely four more points being permuted in addition to $\{1,2,3,4,5,6,7\}$. This yields $n = 10$ or 11 since we must allow for the possibility that point 7 does not occur. However by Lemma 21.3 we cannot have $k = 4$, $n = 10$ and thus $n = 11$.

Step 3. Completion of the proof.

We assume $k \geq 5$ and apply induction on k. Suppose G is sharply k-transitive of degree n. Then G_a is sharply

$(k-1)$-transitive of degree $n-1$. If G_a is trivial, then $|G_a| = (n-1)!$ or $(n-1)!/2$ and hence $|G| = n!$ or $n!/2$. This shows that G is also trivial.

Let us assume that G is nontrivial. If $k = 5$ then G_a is a nontrivial sharply 4-transitive group of degree $n-1$. Hence $n-1 = 11$ and $n = 12$. Similarly $k = 6$ yields $n = 13$. However this group does not exist by Lemma 21.3. It follows easily now that no nontrivial groups exist for $k \geq 6$ and the theorem is proved.

It is not too difficult to show that the groups of degree 11 and 12 above are essentially unique. However we will be content with showing that such groups exist. In fact we will prove the existence of five rather interesting permutation groups, the Mathieu groups. They have degreee 11, 12, 22, 23 and 24. We will use a procedure due to Witt.

LEMMA 21.6. Let G be k-transitive $(k \geq 2)$ on set M. Let $y \in G$ and $b \in M$ with $by \neq b$ and let $x \in Sym(M \cup \{a\})$ with $ax \neq a$. Set $H = \langle G, x \rangle$ and suppose that $x^2 = y^2 = (xy)^3 = 1$ and $xG_bx = G_b$. Then H is

$(k+1)$-transitive on $M \cup \{a\}$ with $H_a = G$.

Proof. Let $K = G \cup GxG$. Then K is nonempty and closed under inverses since $x^2 = 1$. From $x^2 = y^2 = 1$ and $(xy)^3 = 1$ we obtain easily $xyx = yxy$. Now G is doubly transitive so by Proposition 3.7, $G = G_b \cup G_b y G_b$. Hence

$$\begin{aligned} xGx &= x(G_b \cup G_b y G_b)x = xG_b x \cup (xG_b x)xyx(xG_b x) \\ &= G_b \cup G_b xyx G_b = G_b \cup G_b yxy G_b \\ &\subseteq G \cup GxG = K. \end{aligned}$$

This implies easily that K is closed under multiplication and thus $H = K = G \cup GxG$. Since G is transitive on M and $ax \neq a$ we see that H is transitive. Moreover from the double coset decomposition we have clearly $H_a = G$. Finally H_a is k-transitive so H is $(k+1)$-transitive.

LEMMA 21.7. Let G be doubly transitive on M. Let $y \in G$, $a \in M$ with $ay \neq a$ and let $x_1, x_2, x_3 \in \mathrm{Sym}(M \cup \{1, 2, 3$

Suppose that

$$x_1 = (1\ a)(2)(3)\ldots$$

$$x_2 = (1\ 2)(3)(a)\ldots$$

$$x_3 = (2\ 3)(1)(a)\ldots$$

$$y^2 = x_1^{\ 2} = x_2^{\ 2} = x_3^{\ 2} = 1$$

$$(x_1 y)^3 = (x_2 x_1)^3 = (x_3 x_2)^3 = 1$$

$$(y x_2)^2 = (y x_3)^2 = (x_1 x_3)^2 = 1$$

$$x_1 G_a x_1 = x_2 G_a x_2 = x_3 G_a x_3 = G_a.$$

Then $H = \langle G, x_1, x_2, x_3 \rangle$ is 5-transitive on $M \cup \{1, 2, 3\}$ and $H_{123} = G$.

Proof. By the preceding lemma $K = \langle G, x_1 \rangle$ is 3-transitive on $M \cup \{1\}$ with $K_1 = G$. Now $y^2 = (yx_2)^2 = 1$ and $x_2^{\ 2} = 1$ imply that x_2 and y commute and hence

$$x_2 K_1 x_2 = G^{x_2} = \langle G_a, y \rangle^{x_2} = \langle G_a, y \rangle = G = K_1$$

so again by Lemma 21.6, $L = \langle K, x_2 \rangle$ is 4-transitive on $M \cup \{1, 2\}$ with $L_2 = K$. Again we see that x_3 commutes with x_1 and y so

$$x_3 L_2 x_3 = K^{x_3} = \langle G_a, y, x_1 \rangle^{x_3} = \langle G_a, y, x_1 \rangle = K = L_2.$$

Thus $H = \langle L, x_3 \rangle$ is 5-transitive on $M \cup \{1, 2, 3\}$ and $H_3 = L$. Therefore $H_{123} = L_{12} = K_1 = G$.

THEOREM 21.8. Given the following permutations

$$s = (4\ 5\ 6)(7\ 8\ 9)(10\ 11\ 12)$$

$$t = (4\ 7\ 10)(5\ 8\ 11)(6\ 9\ 12)$$

$$u = (5\ 7\ 6\ 10)(8\ 9\ 12\ 11)$$

$$v = (5\ 8\ 6\ 12)(7\ 11\ 10\ 9)$$

$$w = (5\ 11\ 6\ 9)(7\ 12\ 10\ 8)$$

$$x_1 = (1\ 4)(7\ 8)(9\ 11)(10\ 12)$$

$$x_2 = (1\ 2)(7\ 10)(8\ 11)(9\ 12)$$

$$x_3 = (2\ 3)(7\ 12)(8\ 10)(9\ 11).$$

Then $M_{11} = \langle s, t, u, v, w, x_1, x_2 \rangle$ is a sharply 4-transitive group of degree 11 and $M_{12} = \langle M_{11}, x_3 \rangle$ is sharply 5-transitive of degree 12. Thus $|M_{11}| = 7920$ and $|M_{12}| = 95,040$.

Proof. $H = \langle s, t \rangle$ is a regular elementary abelian group of degree 9 which is normalized by $Q = \langle u, v, w \rangle$, a regular group of degree 8 which is quaternion. Moreover Q acts semiregularly on $H^{\#}$. Thus if $G = \langle s, t, u, v, w \rangle$, then $G = HQ$ is a sharply 2-transitive group of degree 9, and $G_4 = Q$.

Let $a = 4$ in the preceding lemma. We see easily that x_1, x_2 and x_3 normalize Q so that

$$G_a^{x_1} = G_a^{x_2} = G_a^{x_3} = G_a.$$

Moreover if $y = s^{-1}u^2 s = (4\ 6)(7\ 12)(8\ 11)(9\ 10)$ then

$$y^2 = x_1^{\ 2} = x_2^{\ 2} = x_3^{\ 2} = 1$$
$$(x_1 y)^3 = (x_2 x_1)^3 = (x_3 x_2)^3 = 1$$
$$(yx_2)^2 = (yx_3)^2 = (x_1 x_3)^2 = 1.$$

Thus Lemma 21.7 implies that M_{12} is 5-transitive of degree 12 and M_{11}, the subgroup fixing point 3, is 4-transitive of degree 11. Since G is the subgroup fixing three points and G is sharply 2-transitive, it follows that M_{12} is sharply 5-transitive and M_{11} is sharply 4-transitive.

Finally we have $|M_{12}| = 12 \cdot 11 \cdot 10 \cdot 9 \cdot 8 = 95{,}040$ and $|M_{11}| = 11 \cdot 10 \cdot 9 \cdot 8 = 7{,}920$ so the result follows.

We use the same procedure to obtain the 5-transitive group M_{24} of degree 24. However we must start with a 2-transitive group of degree 21. We obtain this group and others as follows.

Let q be a prime power. We let $GL(n, q)$ be the group of $n \times n$ nonsingular matrices over $GF(q)$, $SL(n, q)$ the subgroup of those matrices of determinant 1 and $PSL(n, q) = SL(n, q)/\mathfrak{Z}(SL(n, q))$. Let V denote the space of $1 \times n$ row vectors over $GF(q)$. Then certainly $GL(n, q)$ permutes the one-dimensional subspaces of V. Some basic facts are

PROPOSITION 21.9. Let q be a prime power. Then

i. $|GL(n, q)| = (q^n - 1)(q^n - q) \dots (q^n - q^{n-1})$

$|SL(n, q)| = |GL(n, q)|/(q-1)$ and $SL(n, q) \triangle GL(n, q)$

$|PSL(n, q)| = |SL(n, q)|/(n, q-1)$.

ii. If $n > 1$ then $PSL(2, q)$ is a 2-transitive permutation group of degree $(q^n - 1)/(q-1)$. It acts on the one-dimensional subspaces of V.

<u>Proof</u>. We compute $|GL(n,q)|$. Let $g \in GL(n,q)$. The number of choices for the first row of matrix g is clearly (q^n-1). Suppose we have already chosen the first i rows of g to be linearly independent. Then the $(i+1)^{st}$ row cannot be in the i-dimensional subspace spanned by the first i rows. This yields (q^n-q^i) possibilities for the $(i+1)^{st}$ row given the first i. Thus clearly there are $(q^n-1)(q^n-q)\ldots(q^n-q^{n-1})$ possibilities for g and this is $|GL(n,q)|$.

The determinant map is clearly a homomorphism of $GL(n,q)$ onto $GF(q)^{\#}$. The kernel is $SL(n,q)$ so $SL(n,q) \triangle GL(n,q)$ and $[GL(n,q):SL(n,q)] = |GF(q)^{\#}| = q-1$. Now let Z denote the set of scalar matrices in $SL(n,q)$. Then $\lambda I \in Z$ if and only if $\lambda \in GF(q)$ and $\lambda^n = 1$. Thus we have easily $|Z| = (n, q-1)$. If $n = 1$, then clearly $Z = \mathfrak{z}(SL(n,q))$. We will show later that $Z = \mathfrak{z}(SL(n,q))$ for $n > 1$ and this will yield (i).

Now let $n > 1$. Clearly $SL(n,q)$ permutes the 1-dimensional subspaces of V and the kernel is easily seen to be Z. Hence $G = SL(n,q)/Z$ is a faithful permutation group. Its degree is the number of 1-dimensional subspaces of V namely $(q^n-1)/(q-1)$. Let $x_1, x_2, \ldots, x_n$ be the natural basis of V and let V_1 and V_2 be two distinct subspaces, say $V_1 = \langle v_1 \rangle$, $V_2 = \langle v_2 \rangle$. Then v_1 and v_2 are linearly independent and we can extend these to form a basis $v_1, v_2, \ldots, v_n$ of V. Let T_0 be the linear transformation defined by $x_i T_0 = v_i$ so that $T_0 \in GL(n,q)$. If $\lambda = \det T_0$ we define T by $x_1 T = \lambda^{-1} v_1$, $x_i T = v_i$ for $i > 1$. Then $T \in SL(n,q)$ and $\langle x_1 \rangle T = \langle \lambda^{-1} v_1 \rangle = V_1$ and $\langle x_2 \rangle T = \langle v_2 \rangle = V_2$. Thus G is 2-transitive. We show finally that $Z = \mathfrak{z}(SL(n,q))$. Clearly $Z \subseteq \mathfrak{z}(SL(n,q))$. If the inclusion is strict, then G has a nonidentity central subgroup W. Since G is primitive and $W \triangle G$, W is transitive and hence since W is abelian it is a regular normal subgroup of G. This implies that G_a acts transitively on $W^{\#}$ and since W is central we must have $|W^{\#}| = 1$ and $2 = |W| = (q^n-1)/(q-1)$, a contradiction. Thus $Z = \mathfrak{z}(SL(n,q))$, $G = PSL(n,q)$ and the result follows.

THEOREM 21.10. Let $F = GF(2^2) = \{0, 1, d, d^2\}$ and let $G = PSL(3,4)$ act on the 1-dimensional subspaces of a

3-dimensional space over F. We let $[[a, b, c]]$ denote the subspace spanned by the vector $[a, b, c]$ and we let I, II, III be the additional points. Set

$$x_1 = (I, [[1, 0, 0]])h_1$$
$$x_2 = (I, II)h_2$$
$$x_3 = (II, III)h_3$$

where

$$[[a, b, c]]\, h_1 = [[a^2 + bc, b^2, c^2]]$$
$$[[a, b, c]]\, h_2 = [[a^2, b^2, c^2 d]]$$
$$[[a, b, c]]\, h_3 = [[a^2, b^2, c^2]].$$

Then $M_{22} = \langle G, x_1 \rangle$ is a 3-transitive group of degree 22 and order 443,520, $M_{23} = \langle G, x_1, x_2 \rangle$ is a 4-transitive group of degree 23 and order 10,200,960 and $M_{24} = \langle G, x_1, x_2, x_3 \rangle$ is a 5-transitive group of degree 24 and order 244,823,040.

Proof. Let S denote the set of 1-dimensional subspaces so that $|S| = (4^3 - 1)/(4 - 1) = 21$. Now the polynomials appearing in the definition of the h_i are all homogeneous of degree 2. Hence each h_i maps S into S. Further in F the map $x \rightarrow x^2$ is an isomorphism so each h_i is a permutation. Set $1 = [[1,0,0]]$. We see easily that $1h_i = 1$. The point 1 will play the role of a in Lemma 21.7.

Let y be the permutation $[[a,b,c]]y = [[b,a,c]]$. Then y is induced from an element in $GL(3,4)$ with determinant $-1 = 1$ and hence $y \in G$. We now show that x_1, x_2, x_3, y satisfy the assumptions of Lemma 21.7. First they are clearly of the right form. Second it is easy to verify the equations

$$y^2 = x_1^{\ 2} = x_2^{\ 2} = x_3^{\ 2} = 1$$
$$(x_1 y)^3 = (x_2 x_1)^3 = (x_3 x_2)^3 = 1$$
$$(yx_2)^2 = (yx_3)^2 = (x_1 x_3)^2 = 1.$$

It remains to consider $x_i G_1 x_i$.

Let $g \in G_1$. We can clearly assume that

$$[[a,b,c]]\, g = [[a + b\alpha + c\beta,\ b\gamma + c\delta,\ b\sigma + c\tau]]$$

with $\gamma\tau - \delta\sigma = 1$. Certainly $x_i g x_i$ fixes I, II, III and 1 and hence $x_i g x_i = h_i g h_i$. We consider h_1, h_2 and h_3 in turn. Now using the fact that $x^4 = x$ for all $x \in F$ we have easily

$$[\![a,b,c]\!]\, h_1 g h_1 = [\![a+b(\alpha^2+\gamma\sigma)+c(\beta^2+\delta\tau)+b^2c^2(1+\gamma\tau+\delta\sigma),\; b\gamma^2+c\delta^2,\; b\sigma^2+c\tau^2]\!]$$

$$[\![a,b,c]\!]\, h_2 g h_2 = [\![a+b\alpha^2+cd^2\beta^2,\; b\gamma^2+cd^2\delta^2,\; bd\sigma^2+c\tau^2]\!]$$

$$[\![a,b,c]\!]\, h_3 g h_3 = [\![a+b\alpha^2+c\beta^2,\; b\gamma^2+c\delta^2,\; b\sigma^2+c\tau^2]\!].$$

Since $1+\gamma\tau+\delta\sigma = 1-(\gamma\tau-\delta\sigma) = 0$ we see that $h_i g h_i$ is induced from a linear transformation which fixes the vector $[1,0,0]$. We must consider the determinants of these transformations. Since $d^3 = 1$ all three determinants are equal to $\gamma^2\tau^2 - \delta^2\sigma^2 = (\gamma\tau-\delta\sigma)^2 = 1$ and thus $x_i G_1 x_i = G_1$ for all i.

By Proposition 21.9 G is 2-transitive and hence by Lemma 21.7, M_{24} is 5-transitive. Now $|M_{24}| = 24\cdot 23\cdot 22\cdot |G|$ and $|G| = (4^3-1)(4^3-4)(4^3-4^2)/(4-1)^2 = 21\cdot 20\cdot 48$ so $|M_{24}|$ is determined and the result follows.

The groups $M_{11}, M_{12}, M_{22}, M_{23}$ and M_{24} are the five Mathieu groups. We show finally

THEOREM 21.11. The Mathieu groups are simple.

Proof. We proceed in a series of steps.

Step 1. M_{11} is simple.

Set $G = M_{11}$ so that $|G| = 11\cdot 10\cdot 9\cdot 8$. Let $P = \langle x\rangle$ be a subgroup of order 11. Thus P is a Sylow 11-subgroup and x is an 11-cycle. Then P acts transitively. If $A \supseteq P$ and A is abelian, then A is transitive and hence regular so $|A| = |P| = 11$ and $A = P$. Thus P is self centralizing. Since $|\mathrm{Aut}\, P| = 10$, $[\mathfrak{N}(P):P]$ divides 10. Suppose $2 \,\big|\, |\mathfrak{N}(P)|$ and let $y \in \mathfrak{N}(P)$ have order 2. Since the degree is odd, y must fix a point, say 1. Now we must have $x^y = x^{-1}$ so $(1x^r)y = (1y)x^{-r} = 1x^{-r}$. This shows that y is a product of five transpositions and hence $y \notin \mathrm{Alt}(11)$, a contradiction since all generators of M_{11} given in Theorem 21.8 are even permutations. Thus $[\mathfrak{N}(P):P] = 1$ or 5.

Now let $H \triangle G$ with $H \neq \langle 1\rangle$ and $H \neq G$. Since G is primitive, H is transitive and hence $11 \,\big|\, |H|$. Let $|P| = 11$ and $P \subseteq H$. By Proposition 4.8, $G = H\mathfrak{N}_G(P)$ and hence $\mathfrak{N}_G(P) \nsubseteq H$. By the above this implies that $\mathfrak{N}_H(P) = P$ and hence, in H, P is in the center of its normalizer. Thus Theorem 12.7 implies that H has a normal 11-complement K. Then $K \triangle G$ and $11 \nmid |K|$ yields $K = \langle 1\rangle$. Thus $H = P$,

$G = \mathfrak{N}(P)$ and $|G| \leq 55$, a contradiction. Hence M_{11} is simple.

Step 2. PSL(3, 4) is simple.

The proof here is similar to the above with the prime 11 replaced by 7. We consider first the groups SL(3, 4) and GL(3, 4). Their orders are divisible by 7 to the first power only. Hence all subgroups of SL(3, 4) of order 7 are conjugate. Let x be the matrix

$$x = \begin{bmatrix} 0 & 1 & 0 \\ 0 & 0 & 1 \\ 1 & 1 & 0 \end{bmatrix} \in GL(3,4).$$

We see easily that $x^3 = 1 + x$, $x^7 = 1$ and $x \in SL(3,4)$. Thus $\langle x \rangle$ is a Sylow 7-subgroup of SL(3, 4). It is easy to see that all matrices which commute with x are of the form $a + bx + cx^2$ with $a, b, c \in GF(4)$. Thus in GL(3, 4) the centralizer of x has order at most $4^3 - 1$. If $a \in GF(4)$, $a \neq 0$ then $a^3 = 1$ and the matrix $a + x$ has determinant a. This shows that the centralizer of x in $W = SL(3,4)$ has order at most $(4^3 - 1)/(4-1) = 21$. Now $|\mathfrak{Z}(W)| = 3$ so $\mathfrak{C}_W(x) = \mathfrak{Z}(W) \times \langle x \rangle$. If $2 \mid [\mathfrak{N}_W(\langle x \rangle) : \mathfrak{C}_W(x)]$, then x is conjugate to x^{-1} in SL(3,4). This implies that x^{-1} satisfies any polynomial satisfied by x. Thus $x^3 = 1+x$, $x^{-3} = 1+x^{-1}$ and this yields $x = 1$, a contradiction. Hence $[\mathcal{N}_W(\langle x\rangle):\mathcal{C}_W(x)] = 1$ or 3.

Set $G = PSL(3,4)$ and let P be a subgroup of order 7. The inverse image of P in SL(3,4) is $\langle x\rangle \times \mathcal{Z}(W)$ where x and W are as above. This shows easily that $\mathcal{C}_G(P) = P$ and $[\mathcal{N}_G(P):\mathcal{C}_G(P)] = 1$ or 3.

Now let $H \triangle G$ with $H \neq \langle 1\rangle$ and $H \neq G$. Since G is primitive H is transitive of degree 21 and hence $7 \mid |H|$. Let $|P| = 7$ and $P \subseteq H$. By Proposition 4.8, $G = H\mathcal{N}_G(P)$ and hence $\mathcal{N}_G(P) \nsubseteq H$. Thus $\mathcal{N}_H(P) = P$ and hence, in H, P is in the center of its normalizer. Thus by Theorem 12.7 H has a normal 7-complement K. Then $K \triangle G$ and $7 \nmid |K|$ yields $K = \langle 1\rangle$. Thus $H = P$, $G = \mathcal{N}(P)$ and $|G| \leq 21$, a contradiction. Hence PSL(3,4) is simple.

Step 3. The remaining cases.

By Proposition 4.3 none of the groups M_{12}, M_{22}, M_{23} and M_{24} can have a regular normal subgroup since these groups are 3-transitive. We prove the simplicity of these groups inductively using Proposition 4.5. Thus since M_{11} is simple so is M_{12}. Also since PSL(3, 4) is simple we obtain in turn the fact that M_{22}, M_{23} and M_{24} are simple. This completes the proof of the theorem.

REFERENCES

PAPERS

M. Hall Jr., On a theorem of Jordan, Pacific J. Math., 4 (1954) 219-226

G. Higman, Groups and rings having automorphisms without nontrivial fixed elements, J. London Math. Soc., 32 (1957) 321-334

B. Huppert, Zweifach transitive, auflösbare Permutationsgruppen, Math. Zeit., 68 (1957) 126-150

B. Huppert, Scharf dreifach transitive Permutationsgruppen, Arch. Math., 13 (1962) 61-72

I.M. Isaacs and D.S. Passman, Half-transitive automorphism groups, Canad. J. Math., 18 (1966) 1243-1250

D.S. Passman, Solvable half-transitive automorphism groups, J. of Algebra, 6 (1967) 285-304

P. Roquette, Realisierung von Darstellungen endlicher nilpotenter Gruppen, Arch. Math., 9 (1958) 241-250

J.G. Thompson, Normal p-complements for finite groups, J. of Algebra, 1 (1964) 43-46

H. Wielandt, Eine Verallgemeinerung der invarianten Untergruppe, Math. Zeit., 45 (1939) 209-244

H. Wielandt and B. Huppert, Normalteiler mehrfach transitiver Permutationsgruppen, Arch. Math., 9 (1958) 18-26

E. Witt, Die 5-fach transitiven Gruppen von Mathieu, Hamburg Abh., 12 (1938) 256-264

H. Zassenhaus, Kennzeichnung endlicher linearer Gruppen als Permutationsgruppen, Hamburg Abh., 11 (1936) 17-40

H. Zassenhaus, Über endliche Fastkörper, Hamburg Abh., 11 (1936) 187-220

BOOKS

W. Feit, Characters of Finite Groups, Benjamin, New York, N.Y., 1967

W.R. Scott, Group Theory, Prentice-Hall, Englewood Cliffs, N.J., 1964

H. Wielandt, Finite Permutation Groups, Academic Press, New York, N.Y., 1964

H. Zassenhaus, The Theory of Groups, second edition, Chelsea, New York, N.Y., 1958

INDEX